Statistics

S2

James Nicholson

OXFORD
UNIVERSITY PRESS

OXFORD
UNIVERSITY PRESS

Great Clarendon Street, Oxford OX2 6DP

Oxford University Press is a department of the University of Oxford.
It furthers the University's objective of excellence in research, scholarship,
and education by publishing worldwide in

Oxford   New York

Auckland   Cape Town   Dar es Salaam   Hong Kong   Karachi
Kuala Lumpur   Madrid   Melbourne   Mexico City   Nairobi
New Delhi   Shanghai   Taipei   Toronto

With offices in

Argentina   Austria   Brazil   Chile   Czech Republic   France   Greece
Guatemala   Hungary   Italy   Japan   Poland   Portugal   Singapore
South Korea   Switzerland   Thailand   Turkey   Ukraine   Vietnam

British Library Cataloguing in Publication Data

Data available

ISBN-13: 9780-19-911787 1

1 3 5 7 9 10 8 6 4 2

Printed in Great Britain by Ashford Colour Press, Ltd, Gosport.

Paper used in the production of this book is a natural, recyclable product made from
wood grown in sustainable forests. The manufacturing process conforms to the
environmental regulations of the country of origin.

Series Managing Editor Anna Cox

Acknowledgements

The Publisher would like to thank the following for permission to reproduce
photographs:
P20 Ken Rygh Creative Art & Design/iStockphoto; **p22** Darrenw/Dreamstime; **p40**
Stephen Coburn/Shutterstock; **p46** Martia Adelaide Silva/iStockphoto; **p49** Andrew
Howe Photography/iStockphoto; **p76** All-Kind-ZA Photography/iStockphoto; **p86**
peepo/iStockphoto; **p96** David Seymour/Dreamstime; **p116** Fabrizio
Zanier/Dreamstime; **p118** David Chilvers/Alamy; **p120** Philip Wolmoth/Alamy; **p138**
Edyta Pawlowska/Shutterstock.

The Photograph on the cover is reproduced courtesy of George Doyle/Stockbyte/Getty
Images

Series managing editor Anna Cox

The publishers would also like to thank Judy Sadler, Ian Bettison and Charlie Bond for
their expert help in compiling this book.

About this book

Endorsed by Edexcel, this book is designed to help you achieve your best possible grade in Edexcel GCE Mathematics Statistics S2.

Each chapter starts with a list of objectives and a 'Before you start' section to check that you are fully prepared.
Chapters are structured into manageable sections, and there are certain features to look out for within each section:

Key points are highlighted in a blue panel.

Key words are highlighted in bold blue type.

Worked examples demonstrate the key skills and techniques you need to develop.

EXAMPLE 1

If $X \sim \text{Po}(3)$, find $P(X = 2)$.

$$P(X = 2) = \frac{e^{-3}3^2}{2!}$$
$$= 0.224 \text{ (3 s.f.)}$$

Helpful hints are included as blue margin notes and sometimes as blue type within the main text.

Each section includes an exercise with progressive questions, starting with basic practice and developing in difficulty. Some exercises also include 'stretch and challenge' questions marked with a stretch symbol .

At the end of each chapter there is a 'Review' section which includes exam style questions as well as past exam paper questions.

The final page of each chapter gives a summary of the key points, fully cross-referenced to aid revision. Also, a 'Links' feature provides an engaging insight into how the statistics you are studying is relevant to real life.

There are also two Revision Exercises within the book which contain questions spanning a range of topics to give you plenty of realistic exam practice.

At the end of the book you will find full solutions, a key word glossary, a list of essential formulae, statistical tables and an index.

Contents

1

The binomial distribution

This chapter will show you how to
- identify real-life situations which can be modelled by the binomial distribution
- use probability tables (where available) for the binomial distribution
- calculate probabilities for a general binomial distribution
- calculate mean and variance of the binomial distribution.

Before you start

You should know how to:

1 Use your calculator to work out factorials.

2 Substitute values into simple formulae.

Check in:

1 Find the value of

    a   5!

    b $\dfrac{12!}{7!}$

2 Find the value of $M = kx(3 - x)$ when $k = 10$ and $x = 0.4$

1.1 Introducing the binomial distribution

You can use tree diagrams to work out probabilities of events involving separate stages. A special case is where each stage has only two outcomes of interest, and the probabilities of these two outcomes stay the same at each stage.

See **S1** for revision.

Even when there are more than two basic outcomes, you can usually group them into two categories: those which satisfy the event of interest ('success'); and those which do not satisfy it ('failure'). At any stage $P(\text{failure}) = 1 - P(\text{success})$

E.g. If you want to know the probability of obtaining a factor of 6 when you throw a die, then any of the outcomes 1, 2, 3 and 6 result in 'success'.

$P(\text{success}) = \frac{2}{3}$ and $P(\text{failure}) = \frac{1}{3}$

Now look at the probabilities when you roll a die 3 times.

Put these probabilities onto the branches of a tree diagram, and count the number of successes, x, along each path. Some patterns emerge.

Stage 1	Stage 2	Stage 3

$\frac{2}{3}$ S $\quad x = 3, P = \frac{2}{3} \times \frac{2}{3} \times \frac{2}{3}$

$\frac{2}{3}$ S

$\frac{1}{3}$ F $\quad x = 2, P = \frac{2}{3} \times \frac{2}{3} \times \frac{1}{3}$

S

$\frac{1}{3}$ F

$\frac{2}{3}$ S $\quad x = 2, P = \frac{2}{3} \times \frac{1}{3} \times \frac{2}{3}$

$\frac{1}{3}$ F $\quad x = 1, P = \frac{2}{3} \times \frac{1}{3} \times \frac{1}{3}$

$\frac{2}{3}$

$\frac{2}{3}$ S $\quad x = 2, P = \frac{1}{3} \times \frac{2}{3} \times \frac{2}{3}$

$\frac{1}{3}$

$\frac{2}{3}$ S

F $\quad \frac{1}{3}$ F $\quad x = 1, P = \frac{1}{3} \times \frac{2}{3} \times \frac{1}{3}$

$\frac{2}{3}$ S $\quad x = 1, P = \frac{1}{3} \times \frac{1}{3} \times \frac{2}{3}$

$\frac{1}{3}$ F

$\frac{1}{3}$ F $\quad x = 0, P = \frac{1}{3} \times \frac{1}{3} \times \frac{1}{3}$

The three paths with $x = 2$ all have $\frac{2}{3}, \frac{2}{3}$ and $\frac{1}{3}$ multiplied together.

The three paths with $x = 1$ all have $\frac{2}{3}, \frac{1}{3}$ and $\frac{1}{3}$ multiplied together.

There is only one path leading to each of $x = 0$ and $x = 3$.

The number of paths corresponds to the number of ways you can order the three probabilities in each case. The 1, 3, 3, 1 sequence (for $x = 0, 1, 2, 3$) is one of the rows of Pascal's triangle.

You can write the probabilities like this:

$P(x = 0) = 1 \times \left(\frac{1}{3}\right)^3$ $\qquad P(x = 1) = 3 \times \frac{2}{3} \times \left(\frac{1}{3}\right)^2$

$P(x = 2) = 3 \times \left(\frac{2}{3}\right)^2 \times \frac{1}{3}$ $\qquad P(x = 3) = 1 \times \left(\frac{2}{3}\right)^3$

If you extended the tree diagram to six stages, there would be 64 different paths, and it would be really cumbersome to work with.

```
                              1        1
                         1        2        1
                    1        3        3        1
               1        4        6        4        1
          1        5       10       10        5        1
     1        6       15       20       15        6        1
```

You can use the coefficients in Pascal's triangle to write down expressions for the probabilities of getting 0, 1, 2, 3, 4, 5 or 6 successes. These coefficients are called the binomial coefficients.

X	0	1	2	3	4	5	6
$P(X=x)$	$\left(\frac{1}{3}\right)^6$	$6\left(\frac{1}{3}\right)^5\left(\frac{2}{3}\right)$	$15\left(\frac{1}{3}\right)^4\left(\frac{2}{3}\right)^2$	$20\left(\frac{1}{3}\right)^3\left(\frac{2}{3}\right)^3$	$15\left(\frac{1}{3}\right)^2\left(\frac{2}{3}\right)^4$	$6\left(\frac{1}{3}\right)\left(\frac{2}{3}\right)^5$	$\left(\frac{2}{3}\right)^6$

For a six-stage diagram, use the sixth row of Pascal's triangle (the one beginning 1 6 ...).

EXAMPLE 1

If the probability that James is late home from work on any day is 0.4, what is the probability that he is late home twice in a five-day working week?

Use this row in Pascal's triangle: 1, 5, 10, 10, 5, 1
The number of ways of choosing 2 out of 5 is highlighted (the numbers represent how many ways you can choose 0, 1, 2, 3, 4 and 5 out of 5).

P(late twice) = $10 \times 0.4^2 \times 0.6^3$

If James is late twice in the week he will not be late the other three times.

When the number of stages (or trials) is large it is hard to use Pascal's triangle to find the binomial coefficients.

> The number of paths giving r occurrences out of n cases equals the number of ways of choosing r out of n, which is
>
> $$^nC_r = \binom{n}{r} = \frac{n!}{r!(n-r)!}$$

You can also find this from the nth row of Pascal's triangle [the row starting 1 n ...].

Most scientific calculators have a button marked ^nC_r

> The binomial probability distribution is defined as
>
> $$P(X=r) = \binom{n}{r}p^r q^{n-r} \quad \text{for } r = 0, 1, 2, ..., n \quad \text{where } q = 1-p$$

S2

3

There is a family of binomial distributions with two parameters; n, the number of trials, and p, the probability of 'success' for any one trial.

The distribution is often written as $X \sim B(n, p)$.

In Example 1 *if X is the number of times James is late home in a week, then* $X \sim B(5, 0.4)$.

EXAMPLE 2

If $X \sim B(12, 0.2)$ find the probability that $X = 3$.

$$P(X = 3) = \binom{12}{3}(0.2)^3(0.8)^9 = 0.236 \text{ (3 s.f.)}$$

EXAMPLE 3

If $X \sim B(10, 0.9)$ find the probability that $X \leqslant 8$.

Rather than calculate all of the probabilities that x is $0, 1, 2, \ldots, 8$ you can calculate $P(X = 9 \text{ or } 10)$ as the complementary probability and subtract it from 1.

$$P(X \leqslant 8) = 1 - \left[\binom{10}{9}(0.9)^9(0.1) + \binom{10}{10}(0.9)^{10}(0.1)^0\right]$$
$$= 0.264 \text{ (3 s.f.)}$$

EXAMPLE 4

If 25 dice are thrown, find the probability that three 6s are obtained.

If X = number of 6s obtained, then $X \sim B\left(25, \dfrac{1}{6}\right)$

$$P(X = 3) = \binom{25}{3}\left(\frac{1}{6}\right)^3\left(\frac{5}{6}\right)^{22} = 0.193 \text{ (3 s.f.)}$$

You can use a spreadsheet or handheld calculator to work out binomial probabilities when you specify *n*, *p* and the value of *x*.

The formulae and tables booklet has the probabilities for some values of n and p, but not all, so you will need to be able to use the formula as well. Practise using it to improve your confidence and accuracy.

You can use the binomial distribution for any situation where you want to count the number of times a particular outcome is observed out of a fixed number of cases – provided certain conditions are satisfied:

- there is a fixed number of trials
- each trial has the same two possible outcomes
- the outcomes of the trials are independent of one another
- the probability of a 'success' remains constant.

Exercise 1.1

1 **a** Using the first six rows of Pascal's triangle on page 3, write down the next row.

   b Write down the values of

      i $\begin{pmatrix} 7 \\ 3 \end{pmatrix}$ **ii** $^{7}C_{5}$

Make sure you know which elements in the row of Pascal's triangle in part **a** correspond to the calculations in part **b**.

2 **a** Calculate **i** $\begin{pmatrix} 10 \\ 4 \end{pmatrix}$ **ii** $\begin{pmatrix} 9 \\ 0 \end{pmatrix}$ **iii** $\begin{pmatrix} 15 \\ 6 \end{pmatrix}$ **iv** $\begin{pmatrix} 100 \\ 2 \end{pmatrix}$

   b Calculate **i** $^{10}C_{2}$ **ii** $^{11}C_{6}$ **iii** $^{12}C_{12}$ **iv** $^{50}C_{20}$

3 If $X \sim B(6, 0.5)$ find the probability that **i** $X = 2$ **ii** $X = 5$

4 If $X \sim B(6, 0.3)$ find the probability that **i** $X = 2$ **ii** $X = 5$

5 If $X \sim B(12, 0.4)$ find the probability that **i** $X = 3$ **ii** $X = 8$

6 If $X \sim B(12, 0.7)$ find the probability that **i** $X = 3$ **ii** $X = 8$

7 If $X \sim B\left(10, \frac{1}{3}\right)$ find the probability that **i** $X = 0$ **ii** $X = 5$

8 If $X \sim B\left(15, \frac{3}{4}\right)$ find the probability that **i** $X = 7$ **ii** $X = 8$

9 If you toss a fair coin six times find the probability that
   i you get 2 heads **ii** you get 5 heads.

10 If you toss a fair coin ten times calculate the probability that you get:

   a **i** 0 heads   **ii** 1 head   **iii** 2 heads   **iv** 3 heads

   b **i** no more than 1 head
      ii at least 3 heads
      iii more than 3 heads.

Use your answers to part **a** to answer part **b**.

11 If $X \sim B(12, 0.15)$ find **i** $P(X > 2)$ **ii** $P(X \geqslant 10)$

12 If $X \sim B\left(20, \frac{1}{4}\right)$ find **i** $P(X \leqslant 2)$ **ii** $P(X > 19)$

13 Suki has done no revision for a test and has to guess all the answers to 5 multiple choice questions. If there are 4 choices for each question, find the probability she gets

   i none right   **ii** 3 right.

S2

The cumulative probabilities for a number of binomial distributions
are given in tables in the Edexcel formulae booklet.
These tables are reproduced at the back of this book.

The first section is shown here.

BINOMIAL CUMULATIVE DISTRIBUTION FUNCTION

The tabulated value is $P(X \leqslant x)$, where X has a binomial distribution with
index n and parameter p.

$P=$	0.05	0.10	0.15	0.20	0.25	0.30	0.35	0.40	0.45	0.50
$n=5, x=0$	0.7738	0.5905	0.4437	0.3277	0.2373	0.1681	0.1160	0.0778	0.0503	0.0312
1	0.9774	0.9185	0.8352	0.7373	0.6328	0.5282	0.4284	0.3370	0.2562	0.1875
2	0.9988	0.9914	0.9734	0.9421	0.8965	0.8369	0.7648	0.6826	0.5931	0.5000
3	1.0000	0.9995	0.9978	0.9933	0.9844	0.9692	0.9460	0.9130	0.8688	0.8125
4	1.0000	1.0000	0.9999	0.9997	0.9990	0.9976	0.9947	0.9898	0.9815	0.9688
$n=6, x=0$	0.7351	0.5314	0.3771	0.2621	0.1780	0.1176	0.0754	0.0467	0.0277	0.0156
1	0.9672	0.8857	0.7765	0.6554	0.5339	0.4202	0.3191	0.2333	0.1636	0.1094
2	0.9978	0.9842	0.9527	0.9011	0.8506	0.7443	0.6471	0.5443	0.4415	0.3438
3	0.9999	0.9987	0.9941	0.9830	0.9624	0.9295	0.8826	0.8208	0.7447	0.6563
4	1.0000	0.9999	0.9996	0.9984	0.9954	0.9891	0.9777	0.9590	0.9308	0.8906
5	1.0000	1.0000	1.0000	0.9999	0.9998	0.9993	0.9982	0.9959	0.9917	0.9844
$n=7, x=0$	0.6983	0.4783	0.3206	0.2097	0.1335	0.0824	0.0490	0.0280	0.0152	0.0078
1	0.9556	0.8503	0.7166	0.5767	0.4449	0.3294	0.2338	0.1586	0.1024	0.0625
2	0.9962	0.9743	0.9262	0.8520	0.7564	0.6471	0.5323	0.4199	0.3164	0.2266
3	0.9998	0.9973	0.9879	0.9667	0.9294	0.8740	0.8002	0.7102	0.6083	0.5000
4	1.0000	0.9998	0.9988	0.9953	0.9871	0.9712	0.9444	0.9037	0.8471	0.7734
5	1.0000	1.0000	0.9999	0.9996	0.9987	0.9962	0.9910	0.9812	0.9643	0.9375
6	1.0000	1.0000	1.0000	1.0000	0.9999	0.9998	0.9994	0.9984	0.9963	0.9922

This is the cumulative probability distribution
for the $X \sim B(6, 0.2)$ distribution.
The number highlighted in that column has $x=2$,
and gives the probability $P(X \leqslant 2)$.

To find the probability that $X = 2$, use
$$P(X = 2) = P(X \leqslant 2) - P(X \leqslant 1)$$
In the example $P(X = 2) = 0.9011 - 0.6554 = 0.2457$

Be careful when working with 'greater than' probabilities. The general rule is:

$$P(X \geqslant x) = 1 - P(X < x) = 1 - P(X \leqslant (x - 1))$$
$$P(X > x) = 1 - P(X \leqslant x)$$

The tables only show p values up to 0.5. To work with p values higher than this you need to reverse the roles of *success* and *failure*.

Be careful with the limits as well. Listing the numbers of required successes and failures can help.

E.g. If $X \sim B(20, 0.8)$, then you will need to use $Y \sim B(20, 0.2)$, but $P(X \leqslant 17)$ will be the same as $P(Y \geqslant 3) = 1 - P(Y \leqslant 2)$

> When the cumulative probabilities are given to 4 decimal places it is no guarantee that the difference between two of them will also be correct to 4 d.p.

> Here you want 0, 1, 2,..., 16, 17 successes. You can have 3, 4,..., 18, 19, 20 failures, so you exclude only up to and including 2 failures when you use the tables.

EXAMPLE 1

If $X \sim B\left(30, \frac{3}{4}\right)$ find **a** $P(X \leqslant 17)$ **b** $P(X > 24)$

Use $Y \sim B\left(30, \frac{1}{4}\right)$:

The desired probabilities are the same as finding:

a $P(Y \geqslant 13) = 1 - P(Y \leqslant 12) = 1 - 0.9784 = 0.0216$

b $P(Y \leqslant 5) = 0.2026$

Exercise 1.2

1 If $X \sim B(10, 0.2)$ find **a** $P(X \leqslant 3)$ **b** $P(X < 7)$

2 If $X \sim B(12, 0.35)$ find **a** $P(X < 5)$ **b** $P(X > 7)$

3 If $X \sim B(30, 0.4)$ find **a** $P(X \geqslant 14)$ **b** $P(X \leqslant 18)$

4 If $X \sim B(30, 0.7)$ find **a** $P(X > 20)$ **b** $P(X \leqslant 16)$

5 If $X \sim B(50, 0.8)$ find **a** $P(X \geqslant 42)$ **b** $P(X < 30)$

6 On 40% of the days that Sean travels to work he finds he has to stop at a particular set of traffic lights.
Find the probability that he has to stop at these lights no more than five times during a month in which he works 20 days.

> Use the binomial tables for this exercise.

S2

How many 5s would you expect to get on average if you rolled a fair die 120 times?

With a fair die, the probability of getting a 5 on any go is $\frac{1}{6}$, so 'on average' you would expect to see $\frac{1}{6}$ of the throws come up with a 5, i.e. on average there will be twenty 5s in 120 throws.

This does not imply that you expect to get exactly twenty 5s if you throw a fair die 120 times.

If you do a large number of sets of n trials, then the mean of a binomial probability distribution $[X \sim B(n, p)]$ is the average number of successes out of n trials.

p is the probability that any individual trial gives a success, and the proportion of successes in the long term will be equal to p.

See **S1** for revision.

The mean or expected value $E(X)$ and the variance $Var(X)$ of a binomial distribution are as follows:

If $X \sim B(n, p)$, then $E(X) = np$, $Var(X) = (\sigma^2) = npq = np(1 - p)$

Derivations of these results are shown on the next page. You do not need to learn these.

EXAMPLE 1

If $X \sim B(10, 0.2)$ find the mean and variance of X.

$n = 10$ and $p = 0.2$ (so $q = 0.8$) $\Rightarrow np = 2$; $npq = 1.6$

So the mean is 2 and the variance is 1.6.

EXAMPLE 2

If $X \sim B(80, 0.4)$ find the mean and standard deviation of X.

$n = 80$ and $p = 0.4$ (so $q = 0.6$) $\Rightarrow np = 32$; $npq = 19.2$

The mean is 32 and the variance is 19.2, so the standard deviation is $\sqrt{19.2} = 4.38$ to 3 s.f.

The standard deviation is the square root of the variance.

EXAMPLE 3

X is a binomial distribution with mean 8 and variance 6.4. Find $P(X \leqslant 3)$.

$np = 8$, $npq = 6.4 \Rightarrow q = 0.8 \Rightarrow p = 0.2$, $n = 40$

From the $B(40, 0.2)$ tables you get $P(X \leqslant 3) = 0.0285$.

Derivation of mean and variance of the binomial distribution

Let $X \sim B(n, p)$ and $q = 1 - p$

$\Pr\{X = k\} = \dfrac{n!}{k!(n-k)!} p^k q^{n-k}$

By definition $E(X) = \displaystyle\sum_{k=0}^{n} k \times \left[\dfrac{n!}{k!(n-k)!} p^k q^{n-k}\right]$

$\quad = np \displaystyle\sum_{k=1}^{n} \left[\dfrac{(n-1)!}{(k-1)!(n-k)!} p^{k-1} q^{n-k}\right]$

$k = 0$ term is zero. For all other values, k can be cancelled from $k!$

$\quad = np \times \{p + q\}^{n-1} = np \times 1 = np$

The $\sum$ is exactly this binomial expansion.

By definition $E(X^2) = \displaystyle\sum_{k=0}^{n} k^2 \left[\dfrac{n!}{k!(n-k)!} p^k q^{n-k}\right]$

$\quad = np \times \displaystyle\sum_{k=1}^{n} k \left[\dfrac{(n-1)!}{(k-1)!(n-k)!} p^{k-1} q^{n-k}\right]$

$\quad = np \times \displaystyle\sum_{k=1}^{n} (k - 1 + 1) \times \left[\dfrac{(n-1)!}{(k-1)!(n-k)!} p^{k-1} q^{n-k}\right]$

This gives two sums – one you already know:

$\quad = n(n-1)p^2 \times \displaystyle\sum_{k=2}^{n} \left[\dfrac{(n-2)!}{(k-2)!(n-k)!} p^{k-2} q^{n-k}\right] + np$

You can take $k - 1$ out of its factorial, and omit the $k = 1$ term, which is zero.

$\quad = n(n-1)p^2 + np$

So $\mathrm{Var}(X) = n(n-1)p^2 + np - (np)^2 = np(1-p)$ or npq

Exercise 1.3

1 If $X \sim B(35, 0.5)$ find **a** $E(X)$ **b** $\mathrm{Var}(X)$.

2 If $X \sim B(75, 0.4)$ find the mean and standard deviation of X.

3 X is a binomial random variable based on 25 trials. $E(X) = 20$.

  a Find the standard deviation of X.

  b Find $P(X > \mu)$, where $\mu = E(X)$.

4 X is a binomial random variable with $E(X) = 30$ and $\mathrm{Var}(X) = 21$. Find the number of trials.

5 If $X \sim B(20, p)$ find $\mathrm{Var}(X)$ in terms of p. Find the value of p which gives the largest variance.

6 If $X \sim B(8, 0.12)$ find $P(X < \mu - \sigma)$ where $\mu = E(X), \sigma = \sqrt{\mathrm{Var}(X)}$

S2

Modelling with the binomial distribution

If you toss a coin 20 times, how likely are you to get exactly 10 heads?

There is actually less than a 50% chance that a fair coin will show 9, 10 or 11 heads when you toss it 20 times.

You can check this is true using the cumulative tables at the back of this book; the probability is $0.7483 - 0.2517 = 0.4956$.

These graphs show the probabilities for different values of n and p and the effect this has on the shape of the binomial distribution:

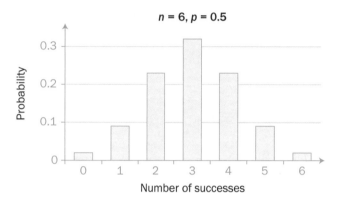

When $p = 0.5$ the distribution is symmetrical and peaks at 3.

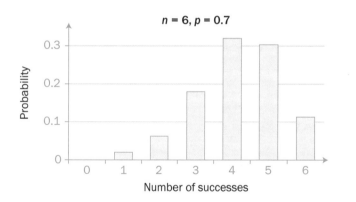

When $p = 0.7$ you would expect to get more successes more often. The distribution peaks at 4 out of 6 successes.
About three or four of the probabilities are relatively high, with the largest individual probabilities somewhere around $\frac{1}{3}$.

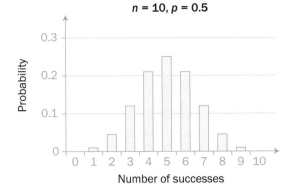

If *n* is increased to 10, a larger number of outcomes have relatively high probabilities, but since the total probability is 1 the largest probabilities cannot be as high as in the previous cases.

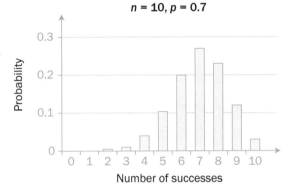

With *p* slightly larger than 0.5, the distribution will be slightly skewed with a tail of smaller probabilities for low numbers of successes.

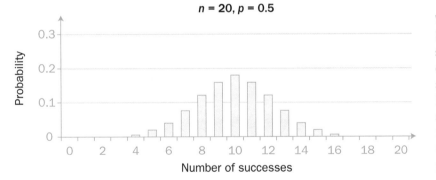

With a larger value of *n* (here it is 20) and $p = 0.5$ the graph is symmetric with again about half of the possible number of successes contributing relatively high probabilities – the highest single probability is less than 1 in 5, and the total probability of getting 9, 10 or 11 successes is less than $\frac{1}{2}$.

S2

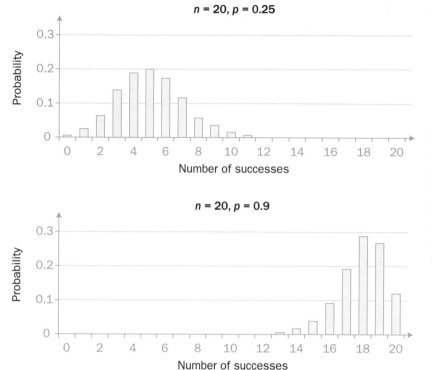

When the value of p is reduced or increased, the peak of the distribution moves left or right. When p moves further from $\frac{1}{2}$, the distribution peak gets higher and the distribution becomes less spread out (lower variance).

The conditions for the binomial distribution are:

1 there has to be a fixed number of trials
2 each trial must have the same two possible outcomes
3 the outcomes of the trials have to be independent
4 the probability of a 'success' remains constant.

An experiment in which you tossed a coin until you obtained 10 heads would not have a fixed number of trials.

Conditions 3 and 4 are closely related. Independence is a very strong condition. However, sometimes outcomes might be assumed to be independent when they are not.

In these examples conditions 3 and 4 do *not* hold:

If a group of sixth-formers arrive together for lunch in school, their choice of meal or the subjects they study are not likely to be independent.

The lessons being taught before lunch will affect which students arrive for lunch together. Students' meal choices may be affected by what food their friends choose.

In cases where a task is performed repeatedly, the probability of success might increase with practice.

Assuming that a golfer finishes each hole on a golf course in the same number of shots ignores a lot of features.

The length of a hole and the difficulty level may vary quite a lot.

Independence does not hold if sampling takes place without replacement. In a population of size N, the second observation comes from the reduced population of size $N - 1$, and so on. The larger the population is to start with, the less error is introduced by assuming that the probability remains fixed at the starting proportions. When n is large you can sometimes use the binomial distribution as an approximation even if it isn't exactly right.

The binomial distribution is a good model for many real-life situations, for example in digital communications and genetics.

Summary of properties of the binomial distribution

The parameters of the binomial distribution $X \sim B(n, p)$ are n (the number of trials) and p (the probability of a 'success' on any single trial).

The conditions to be satisfied are:

- a fixed number of trials
- each trial must have the same two possible outcomes
- independence of trials
- a constant probability of success.

The probability distribution is

$$P(X = k) = \binom{n}{r} p^r q^{n-r} \quad \text{where} \quad \binom{n}{r} = {}^nC_r = \frac{n!}{r!(n-r)!}$$

for integer values k from 0 up to n.

Mean, $E(X) = np$; variance, $\text{Var}(X) = npq$ (where $q = 1 - p$)

S2

Exercise 1.4

1 For the following random variables state whether they can be modelled by a binomial distribution. If they can, give the values of the parameters n and p; if they cannot then explain why.

   a A die is thrown repeatedly until a 1 is seen.
     $X =$ number of throws.

   b A die is thrown 10 times. $X =$ number of 1s seen.

   c A bag has 25 red and 25 blue balls in it. Five balls are taken out without replacement.
     $X =$ the number of red balls taken.

   d $X =$ number of boys in a family of five children.

   e A pair of dice is thrown 25 times.
     $X =$ number of times a double is thrown.

   f A pair of dice is thrown 25 times.
     $X =$ average score of the sum of the numbers showing.

2 a If $X \sim B(30, 0.1)$, use the binomial probability tables to find the probability that X is exactly

    i 0   ii 1

    iii 2   iv 3

   b State the mode of X.

   c Give the mean and variance of X.

3 a If $X \sim B(25, 0.3)$, use the binomial probability tables to find the probability that X is exactly

    i 6   ii 7

    iii 8   iv 9

   b State the mode of X.

   c Give the mean and variance of X.

4 For the following situations state what assumptions are needed if a binomial distribution is to be used to model them, and give the values of *n* and *p* that would be used.

You are *not* expected to do any calculations.

  a On average a traffic warden gives a parking ticket to 8% of the cars he checks. One morning he checks 40 cars. How many tickets does he give out that morning?

  b A box has 48 matches in it. On average, 2% of the matches made by that manufacturer do not strike properly. How many matches from the box will not strike properly?

  c A bag has 5 red, 3 blue and 2 green balls in it. Balls are taken out and the colour noted before the ball is returned. This is done 50 times.
  How many times was a blue ball taken out?

  d A large drum has coloured balls in it. 50% are red, 30% are blue and 20% are green. 50 balls are removed and the number of blue balls is counted.

5 A vet thinks that the number of male puppies in litters of a given size will follow a binomial distribution with $p = 0.5$.

  a In litters of six puppies, what would be the mean and variance of the number of males if the distribution is binomial?

The vet records the number of males in 82 litters of six puppies, and the results are summarised in the table.

Number of males	0	1	2	3	4	5	6
Frequency	8	10	16	15	14	12	7

  b Calculate the mean and variance of the number of males in litters of six puppies.

  c Do you think the binomial distribution is a good model for the number of males in a litter of puppies?

6 $X \sim B(40, p)$ and Var $(X) = 9.6$.

  a Find the two possible values of *p*.

  b For each of the values of *p* find $P(X < \mu - \sigma)$.

S2

1 A quality control agent tests sets of 10 components from a production line which is known to produce 98% good components.

   a   Find the probability that a set chosen at random is free from defects.

   b   If the quality control agent tests five sets before lunch, find the probability that four of these sets were free from defects.

   c   The agent tests 70 sets in a week's work. On average, how many sets does she find which are not perfect?

2 a   A student taking a multiple choice test has done no work on this part of the course. The test has 20 questions, each with a choice of 5 answers. She decides to guess at random. Find the probability that she gets less than 4 correct.

   b   Another student taking the same test has done a little work, and finds that he knows the correct answers to a quarter of the questions. In each of the other questions he can rule out 3 of the given answers, but then has to guess.

      i   Find the probability that he scores more than half marks overall.

      ii Find the probability that he gets no more than 3 wrong.   [(c) Edexcel Limited 2005]

3 It is estimated that 4% of people have green eyes. In a random sample of size n, the expected number of people with green eyes is 5.

   a   Calculate the value of n.

The expected number of people with green eyes in a second random sample is 3.

   b   Find the standard deviation of the number of people with green eyes in this second sample.

4 A recent survey suggested that the proportion of 15-year-old girls who never consider their health when deciding what to eat is 0.1. Assuming that this figure is accurate, what is the probability that in a random sample of thirty 15-year-old girls the number who never consider their health when deciding what to eat is

   a   4 or fewer   b   exactly 4?

5 Each evening Louise sets her alarm for 7.30 a.m.
  She believes that the probability that she wakes before her alarm
  rings each morning is 0.4, and is independent from day to day.

  a Assuming that Louise's belief is correct, determine the
    probability that, during a week (5 mornings), she wakes before
    her alarm rings
    i   on 2 or fewer mornings
    ii on more than 1 but fewer than 4 mornings.

  b Assuming that Louise's belief is correct, calculate the probability
    that, during a 4-week period, she wakes before her alarm rings
    on exactly 7 mornings.

  c Assuming that Louise's belief is correct, calculate values for the
    mean and standard deviation of the number of mornings in a
    week when Louise wakes before her alarm rings.

  d During a 50-week period, Louise records, each week, the number
    of mornings on which she wakes before her alarm rings.
    The results are as follows.

Number of mornings	0	1	2	3	4	5
Frequency	10	11	9	9	6	5

  i   Calculate the mean and standard deviation of these data.
  ii State, giving reasons, whether your answers to part **d i** support
      Louise's belief that the probability that she wakes before her
      alarm rings each morning is 0.4, and is independent from
      morning to morning.

6 The table below shows, for a particular population, the proportions
  of people in each of the four main blood groups.

Blood group	O	A	B	AB
Proportion	0.40	0.28	0.20	0.12

  A random sample of 40 people is selected.

  a Determine the probability that the sample contains:
    i   at most 10 people with blood group B
    ii exactly 5 people with blood group AB
    iii more than 10 but fewer than 20 people with blood group O.

  b A random sample of 750 people is selected from the population.
    Find the values for the mean and variance of the number of people
    in the sample with blood group A.

S2

7 Ronnie and Chris regularly play each other at tennis.

   a The probability that Ronnie wins any game is 0.3, and the outcome of each game is independent of the outcome of every other game.

Find the probability that, in a match of 15 games, Ronnie wins:
    i exactly 4 games
    ii fewer than half of the games
    iii exactly half of the games
    iv more than 1 but fewer than 6 games.

   b Ronnie attends tennis coaching sessions for three months. He then claims that the probability of him winning any game is 0.6, and that the outcome of each game is independent of the outcome of every other game.

    i Assuming this claim to be true, calculate the mean and standard deviation for the number of games won by Ronnie in a match of 15 games.
    ii To assess Ronnie's claim, Chris keeps a record of the number of games won by Ronnie in a series of 10 matches, each of the 15 games with these results:

       9   11   7   10   9   12   8   7   8   10

    Calculate the mean and standard deviation of these values.
    iii Hence comment on the validity of Ronnie's claim.

8 Plastic clothes pegs are made in several colours.
The number of blue pegs may be modelled by a binomial distribution with parameter p equal to 0.2.
The contents of packets of 40 pegs of several colours may be considered to be random samples.

   a Determine the probability that a packet contains:

    i at most 10 blue pegs
    ii exactly 10 blue pegs
    iii more than 5 but fewer than 15 blue pegs.

   b Con, a statistics student, claims to have counted the number of blue pegs in each of 100 packets of 40 pegs as part of a homework assignment. From his results these values are calculated:

    Mean number of blue pegs per packet = 8.5
    Variance of number of blue pegs per packet = 18.32

   Comment on the validity of Con's claim.

9 Jakob is a dentist who finds that, on average, one in five of his patients do not turn up for their appointment.

   a Using a binomial distribution find the mean and variance of the number of patients who turn up for their appointment in a clinic where there were 20 appointments.

   b Find the probability that more than 3 patients do not turn up for their appointment in that clinic.

10 Copies of an advertisement for a course in practical statistics are sent to mathematics teachers in a county. For each teacher who receives a copy, the probability of subsequently attending the course is 0.07.
Eighteen teachers receive a copy of the advertisement.
What is the probability that the number who subsequently attend the course will be

   a 2 or fewer

   b exactly 4?

11 **a** State *two* assumptions of the binomial distribution.

   b A small Christmas decoration contains four electric light bulbs.

The probability that a bulb is faulty is 0.09.

     i What is the probability that exactly two bulbs are faulty?
     ii What is the probability that at least one is faulty?

   c A set of Christmas tree lights consist of 20 light bulbs connected so that if at least one is faulty then none of the bulbs will light. The probability that a fitted bulb is faulty is p.
Show that if $p = 0.034$ there is approximately a 50:50 chance that the Christmas tree lights do not light.

12 In a set of coloured beads used in costume jewellery 10% are purple.

   a Find the probability that in a string of 30 beads two or fewer beads are purple.

   b Calculate the probability that in a string of 32 beads exactly two beads are purple.

   c State *one* assumption that you have made in answering parts **a** and **b**.

S2

Summary

Refer to

- The binomial distribution has two parameters, n – the number of trials and p – the probability of a success on any trial.
  - The number of outcomes giving r occurrences out of n cases is

$$^nC_r = \binom{n}{r} = \frac{n!}{r!(n-r)!}$$

  - $P(X = r) = \binom{n}{r} p^r q^{n-r}$ for $r = 0, 1, 2 \ldots n$ 1.1

- The binomial distribution requires certain conditions:
  - there has to be a fixed number of trials
  - each trial must have the same two possible outcomes
  - the outcomes of the trials have to be independent of one another
  - the probability of a 'success' has to remain constant. 1.1

  If these conditions are not met completely the binomial distribution may still provide a reasonable model. 1.4

- The probability tables for the binomial distribution give the cumulative probability for certain values of n for values of p in increments of 0.05. If p is > 0.5, then you need to count the number of failures using the value of $1 - p$. 1.2

- If $X \sim B(n, p)$, then $E(X) = np$; $Var(X) = (\sigma)^2 = npq = np(1 - p)$ 1.3

Links

The binomial distribution is used in many aspects of modern technology, including digital systems.

Digital messages are transmitted as sequences of signals, which can be represented by the binary digits 0 or 1.

Noise can occur when the signal is being transmitted, while the signal is in transmission, or while the signal is being received, and can distort the message.

The number of errors in messages is modeled by a binomial distribution. By understanding how the errors are distributed, systems designers can try to minimise the effects of the noise.

2

The Poisson distribution

This chapter will show you how to
- identify real-life situations which can be modelled by the Poisson distribution
- use probability tables for the Poisson distribution where available
- calculate probabilities for a general Poisson distribution
- work with the mean and variance of the Poisson distribution
- approximate a binomial distribution by a Poisson distribution.

Before you start

You should know how to:

1 Use your calculator to work out values of exponential functions.

2 Evaluate expressions involving the exponential function.

Check in:

1 Find the value of

   a e^{-3}

   b $e^{-2.1}$

2 Find the value of
   $$p = \frac{e^{-3} \times 3^5}{5!}$$

Think about the following random variables:

- the number of dandelions in a square metre of open ground
- the number of errors in a page of a typed manuscript
- the number of cars passing under a bridge on a motorway in a minute (when there is no traffic interference on the motorway)
- the number of telephone calls received by a company switchboard in half an hour.

Do these random variables have any features in common?

The behaviour of these random variables follows the Poisson distribution.

Formally, the conditions for a Poisson distribution are that:

1 events occur at random
2 events occur independently of one another
3 the average rate of occurrences remains constant
4 there is zero probability of simultaneous occurrences.

The Poisson distribution is defined as

$$P(X = r) = \frac{e^{-\lambda}\lambda^r}{r!} \quad \text{for } r = 0, 1, 2, 3, \dots$$

There is a family of Poisson distributions with only one parameter, λ, which is the mean number of occurrences in the time period (or length, or area) being considered.

You can write the Poisson distribution as $X \sim \text{Po}(\lambda)$.

EXAMPLE 1

If $X \sim \text{Po}(3)$, find $P(X = 2)$.

$$P(X = 2) = \frac{e^{-3}3^2}{2!}$$
$$= 0.224 \text{ (3 s.f.)}$$

S2

EXAMPLE 2

The number of cars passing a point on a road during a 5-minute period may be modelled by the Poisson distribution with parameter 4.

Find the probability that in a 5-minute period

a 2 cars go past **b** fewer than 3 cars go past.

- -

$X \sim \text{Po}(4)$

a $P(X = 2) = \dfrac{e^{-4}4^2}{2!} = 0.146\,525\ldots = 0.147$ (3 s.f.)

b $P(X = 0) = \dfrac{e^{-4}4^0}{0!} = 0.01\,831\ldots = 0.0183$ (3 s.f.)

$P(X = 1) = \dfrac{e^{-4}4^1}{1!} = 0.07\,326\ldots = 0.0733$ (3 s.f.)

$P(X \leqslant 2) = 0.01\,831\ldots + 0.07\,326\ldots + 0.146\,525\ldots$
$= 0.238$ (3 s.f.)

The formulae and tables booklet has the probabilities for some values of λ, but not all, so you need to be able to use the formula as well. Practise using it to improve your confidence and accuracy.

Exercise 2.1

1 If $X \sim \text{Po}(2)$ find **a** $P(X = 1)$ **b** $P(X = 3)$

2 If $X \sim \text{Po}(1.8)$ find **a** $P(X = 3)$ **b** $P(X = 2)$

3 If $X \sim \text{Po}(5.3)$ find **a** $P(X = 3)$ **b** $P(X = 7)$

4 If $X \sim \text{Po}(0.4)$ find **a** $P(X = 0)$ **b** $P(X = 1)$

5 If $X \sim \text{Po}(2.15)$ find **a** $P(X = 2)$ **b** $P(X = 4)$

6 If $X \sim \text{Po}(3.2)$ find **a** $P(X = 2)$ **b** $P(X \leqslant 2)$

7 The number of telephone calls arriving at an office switchboard in a 5-minute period may be modelled by a Poisson distribution with parameter 3.2. Find the probability that in a 5-minute period

a exactly 2 calls are received **b** more than 2 calls are received.

8 The number of accidents which occur on a particular stretch of road in a day may be modelled by a Poisson distribution with parameter 1.3. Find the probability that on a particular day

a exactly 2 accidents occur **b** fewer than 2 accidents occur.

S2

The mean number of events in an interval of time or space is proportional to the size of the interval.

This is true as long as the average rate of occurrences remains constant.

In Example 2 in Section 2.1 the number of cars passing a point on a road during a 5-minute period was modelled by the Poisson distribution with parameter 4.

The number of cars passing that point in a 20-minute period may be modelled by the Poisson distribution with parameter 16, and in a one-minute period it may be modelled by the Poisson distribution with parameter 0.8.

If the conditions for a Poisson distribution are satisfied in a given period, they are also satisfied for periods of different length.

The average rate must be constant throughout.

EXAMPLE 1

The number of accidents in a week on a stretch of road is known to follow a Poisson distribution with parameter 2.1. Find the probability that

a in a given week there is 1 accident

b in a two-week period there are 2 accidents

c there is 1 accident in each of two successive weeks.

-----

a In one week, the number of accidents follows a Po(2.1) distribution, so

the probability of 1 accident $= \dfrac{e^{-2.1}2.1^1}{1!} = 0.257\,(3\,\text{s.f.})$

b In two weeks, the number of accidents follows a Po(4.2) distribution,

so the probability of 2 accidents $= \dfrac{e^{-4.2}4.2^2}{2!} = 0.132\,(3\,\text{s.f.})$

c This cannot be done directly as a Poisson distribution since it concerns what happens in each of two time periods, but these are the outcomes considered in part **a**.

So the probability this happens in two successive weeks is

$\left(\dfrac{e^{-2.1}2.1^1}{1!}\right)^2 = 0.0661\,(3\,\text{s.f.})$

Compare your answers to parts **b** and **c**. The probability in part **b** is higher because it includes one accident occuring in each week and also the cases where two accidents occur in one week and no accidents occur in the other week.

EXAMPLE 2

The number of flaws in a metre length of dress material is known to follow a Poisson distribution with parameter 0.4. Find the probabilities that

a there are no flaws in a 1-metre length

b there is 1 flaw in a 3-metre length

c there is 1 flaw in a half-metre length.

---

a $X \sim \text{Po}(0.4) \Rightarrow P(X = 0) = \dfrac{e^{-0.4} \times 0.4^0}{0!} = 0.670\,(3\,\text{s.f.})$

b $Y \sim \text{Po}(1.2) \Rightarrow P(Y = 1) = \dfrac{e^{-1.2} \times 1.2^1}{1!} = 0.361\,(3\,\text{s.f.})$

c $Z \sim \text{Po}(0.2) \Rightarrow P(Z = 1) = \dfrac{e^{-0.2} \times 0.2^1}{1!} = 0.164\,(3\,\text{s.f.})$

While all three of these calculations relate to the same basic situation, they all use different Poisson distributions. Using different variables avoids confusion.

Exercise 2.2

1 The number of telephone calls arriving at an office switchboard in a 5 minute period may be modelled by a Poisson distribution with parameter 1.4. Find the probability that in a 10 minute period

a exactly 2 calls are received

b more than 2 calls are received.

2 The number of accidents which occur on a particular stretch of road in a day may be modelled by a Poisson distribution with parameter 0.3. Find the probability that during a week (7 days)

a exactly 2 accidents occur on that stretch of road

b fewer than 2 accidents occur on that stretch of road.

3 The number of letters delivered to a house on a day may be modelled by a Poisson distribution with parameter 0.8.

a Find the probability that there are 2 letters delivered on a particular day.

b The home owner is away for 3 days. Find the probability that there will be more than 2 letters waiting for him when he gets back.

4 The number of errors on a page of a booklet can be modelled by a Poisson distribution with parameter 0.2.

a Find the probability that there is exactly 1 error on a given page.

b A section of the booklet has 7 pages. Find the probability that there are no more than 2 errors in the section.

c The booklet has 25 pages altogether. Find the probability that the booklet contains exactly 6 errors altogether.

The recurrence relation for the Poisson distribution

You can calculate probabilities for a Poisson distribution in sequence using a recurrence relation.

EXAMPLE 1

If $X \sim \text{Po}(\lambda)$

a write down the probability that
 i $X = 3$ **ii** $X = 4$
b express $P(X = 4)$ in terms of $P(X = 3)$.

- -

a i $P(X = 3) = \dfrac{e^{-\lambda} \times \lambda^3}{3!}$

 ii $P(X = 4) = \dfrac{e^{-\lambda} \times \lambda^4}{4!}$

b $\dfrac{e^{-\lambda} \times \lambda^4}{4!} = \left(\dfrac{e^{-\lambda} \times \lambda^3}{3!} \right) \times \dfrac{\lambda}{4}$

so $P(X = 4) = P(X = 3) \times \dfrac{\lambda}{4}$

$4! = 4 \times (3 \times 2 \times 1) = 4 \times 3!$

The general recurrence relation for a Poisson distribution is

$$P(X = k + 1) = \frac{\lambda}{k + 1} \times P(X = k)$$

The following graphs show the probability distributions for different values of λ and what effect this has on the shape of a particular Poisson distribution.

All Poisson variables have an outcome space which is all of the non-negative integers.

Poisson, λ = 1.2 {= E(x)}

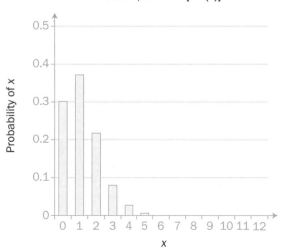

When λ is relatively low, the probabilities tail off very quickly. In this example the mode is 1.

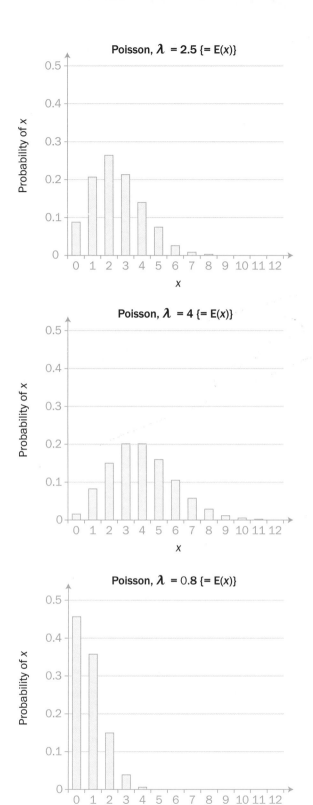

Here λ is larger than in the previous graph, and the peak has moved to the right.
More values of X have a noticeable probability, so the highest individual probability is not as large as it was in the previous graph and the distribution is more spread out.

What happens when λ is an integer?
Generally, the mode of the Poisson (λ) distribution is at the integer below λ when λ is not an integer and there are two modes (at λ and $\lambda - 1$) when λ is an integer.

S2

$\lambda < 1$ is a special case.
The mode will be 0 and the probability distribution is strictly decreasing for all values of X.

The general forms for the probabilities of 0 and 1 for a Poisson distribution are

$$P(X = 0) = \frac{e^{-\lambda} \times \lambda^0}{0!} = e^{-\lambda} \quad \text{and} \quad P(X = 1) = \frac{e^{-\lambda} \times \lambda^1}{1!} = \lambda e^{-\lambda}$$

EXAMPLE 2

$X \sim \text{Po}(\lambda)$ and $P(X = 6) = 2 \times P(X = 5)$.
Find the value of λ.

$P(X = 6) = \frac{\lambda}{6} \times P(X = 5)$ so $\frac{\lambda}{6} = 2$ and $\lambda = 12$

EXAMPLE 3

$X \sim \text{Po}(5.8)$. State the mode of X.

The mode is the integer below 5.8, i.e. the mode is 5.

This graph shows how the Poisson distribution changes when λ is large:

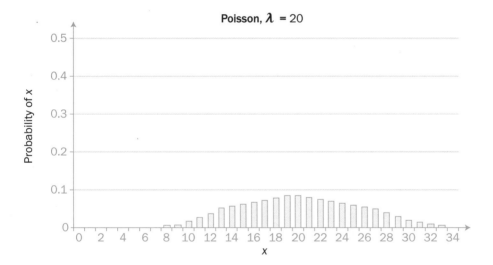

With $\lambda = 20$, the individual probabilities are becoming very small, and the ones which are relatively likely have moved a long way to the right of the graph – where they are still clustered around the mean (now 20).

Exercise 2.3

1 $X \sim \text{Po}(2.5)$

   a Write down an expression for $P(X = 4)$ in terms of $P(X = 3)$.

   b If $P(X = 3) = 0.214$, calculate the value of your expression in part **a**.

   c Calculate $P(X = 4)$ directly and check that it is the same as your answer to **b**.

   d What is the mode of X?

2 $X \sim \text{Po}(4)$

   a Write down an expression for $P(X = 4)$ in terms of $P(X = 3)$.

   b Explain why X has two modes at 3 and 4.

3 $X \sim \text{Po}(\lambda)$ and $P(X = 4) = 1.2 \times P(X = 3)$

   a Find the value of λ.

   b What is the mode of X?

4 $X \sim \text{Po}(6.5)$

   a Write down an expression for $P(X = 7)$ in terms of $P(X = 6)$.

   b Explain why X has its mode at 6.

5 $X \sim \text{Po}(\lambda)$ and $P(X = 10) = 0.9 \times P(X = 87)$

   a Find the value of λ.

   b What is the mode of X?

S2

The cumulative probabilities for the Poisson distributions up to $\lambda = 10.0$ in increments of 0.5 are given in the Edexcel formulae tables. (These tables are reproduced at the back of this book.) If λ is greater than 10, or not one of the values in the table, you will need to use the formula to calculate probabilities.

The Poisson distribution has only one parameter, λ, so the tables are simpler than for the binomial distribution.

POISSON CUMULATIVE DISTRIBUTION FUNCTION

The tabulated value is $P(X \leqslant x)$, where X has a Poisson distribution with parameter λ.

$\lambda =$	0.5	1.0	1.5	2.0	2.5	3.0	3.5	4.0	4.5	5.0
$x = 0$	0.6065	0.3679	0.2231	0.1353	0.0821	0.0498	0.0302	0.0183	0.0111	0.0067
1	0.9098	0.7358	0.5578	0.4060	0.2873	0.1991	0.1359	0.0916	0.0611	0.0404
2	0.9856	0.9197	0.8088	0.6767	0.5438	0.4232	0.3208	0.2381	0.1736	0.1247
3	0.9982	0.9810	0.9344	0.8571	0.7576	0.6472	0.5366	0.4335	0.3423	0.2650
4	0.9998	0.9963	0.9814	0.9473	0.8912	0.8153	0.7254	0.6288	0.5321	0.4405
5	1.0000	0.9994	0.9955	0.9834	0.9580	0.9161	0.8576	0.7851	0.7029	0.6160
6	1.0000	0.9999	0.9991	0.9955	0.9858	0.9665	0.9347	0.8893	0.8311	0.7622
7	1.0000	1.0000	0.9998	0.9989	0.9958	0.9881	0.9733	0.9489	0.9134	0.8666
8	1.0000	1.0000	1.0000	0.9998	0.9989	0.9962	0.9901	0.9786	0.9597	0.9319
9	1.0000	1.0000	1.0000	1.0000	0.9997	0.9989	0.9967	0.9919	0.9829	0.9682
10	1.0000	1.0000	1.0000	1.0000	0.9999	0.9997	0.9990	0.9972	0.9933	0.9863
11	1.0000	1.0000	1.0000	1.0000	1.0000	0.9999	0.9997	0.9991	0.9976	0.9945

This is the cumulative probability distribution for the $X \sim Po(2.0)$ distribution. The number highlighted in that column has $x = 4$, and gives the probability $P(X \leqslant 4)$.

To find the probability that $X = 4$, you can use
$P(X = 4) = P(X \leqslant 4) - P(X \leqslant 3)$
which in this example would be
$0.9473 - 0.8571 = 0.0902$

Take care with the accuracy of this probability.

As with the binomial distribution, when you work with probabilities for $<$, $>$ and $\geqslant$ you need to be careful about using the correct cumulative probability.

EXAMPLE 1

If $X \sim \text{Po}(8.5)$ find
a $P(X < 7)$ **b** $P(X \geqslant 9)$ **c** $P(X > 4)$ **d** $P(4 < X < 9)$

Use the $X \sim \text{Po}(8.5)$ tables:
a $P(X < 7) = P(X \leqslant 6) = 0.2562$

b $P(X \geqslant 9) = 1 - P(X \leqslant 8) = 1 - 0.5231 = 0.4769$

c $P(X > 4) = 1 - P(X \leqslant 4) = 1 - 0.0744 = 0.9256$

d $P(4 < X < 9) = P(X < 9) - P(X \leqslant 4) = 0.5231 - 0.0301 = 0.493$

Exercise 2.4

1 If $X \sim \text{Po}(2.5)$ find   **a** $P(X \leqslant 3)$ **b** $P(X < 7)$ **c** $P(3 < X < 7)$ Use the Poisson tables for this exercise.

2 If $X \sim \text{Po}(6.0)$ find   **a** $P(X < 5)$ **b** $P(X > 7)$ **c** $P(5 < X \leqslant 7)$

3 If $X \sim \text{Po}(10)$ find   **a** $P(X \geqslant 14)$ **b** $P(X \leqslant 18)$ **c** $P(14 < X < 18)$

4 If $X \sim \text{Po}(6.5)$ find   **a** $P(X > 3)$ **b** $P(X \leqslant 6)$ **c** $P(3 \leqslant X \leqslant 6)$

5 If $X \sim \text{Po}(4.5)$ find   **a** $P(X \geqslant 4)$ **b** $P(X \leqslant 4)$ **c** $P(4 \leqslant X \leqslant 4)$

6 The number of telephone calls arriving at an office switchboard in a 5 minute period may be modelled by a Poisson distribution with parameter 2.5. Find the probability that
   a in a 5-minute period exactly 4 calls are received

   b fewer than 6 calls are received in a quarter of an hour.

7 The number of accidents which occur on a particular stretch of road in a day may be modelled by a Poisson distribution with parameter 0.5. Find the probability that during a week (7 days)
   a exactly 5 accidents occur on that stretch of road

   b not more than 5 accidents occur on that stretch of road.

8 The number of letters delivered to a house on a day may be modelled by a Poisson distribution with parameter 2.5.
   a Find the probability that there are 2 letters delivered on a particular day.

   b The home owner is away for 3 days. Find the probability that there will be more than 8 letters waiting for him when he gets back.

9 The number of errors on a page of a booklet can be modelled by a Poisson distribution with parameter 0.2. The booklet has 40 pages altogether. Find the probability that the booklet contains at least 10 errors.

S2

If $X \sim \text{Po}(\lambda)$, then $\text{E}(X) = \lambda$; $\text{Var}(X) = \lambda \Rightarrow$ standard deviation, $\sigma = \sqrt{\lambda}$

A special property of the Poisson distribution is that the mean and variance are always equal.

EXAMPLE 1

The number of calls arriving at a switchboard in a 10-minute period can be modelled by a Poisson distribution with parameter 3.5. Give the mean and variance of the number of calls which arrive in

a 10 minutes   b an hour   c 5 minutes

a $\lambda = 3.5$ so the mean and variance will both be 3.5.

b $\lambda = 21 \ (= 3.5 \times 6)$ so the mean and variance will both be 21.

c $\lambda = 1.75 \ (= 3.5 \div 2)$ so the mean and variance will both be 1.75.

EXAMPLE 2

A dual carriageway has one lane blocked off due to roadworks. The number of cars passing a point in a road in a number of one-minute intervals is summarised in the table.

Number of cars	0	1	2	3	4	5	6
Frequency	3	4	4	25	30	3	1

a Calculate the mean and variance of the number of cars passing in one minute intervals.

b Is the Poisson distribution likely to be an adequate model for the distribution of the number of cars passing in one-minute intervals?

a $\sum f = 70$, $\sum xf = 228$ $\sum x^2 f = 836$, so $\bar{x} = \frac{228}{70} = 3.26 \ (3 \text{ s.f.})$

and $\text{Var}(X) = \frac{\sum x^2 f}{\sum f} - \bar{x}^2 = \frac{836}{70} - \left(\frac{228}{70}\right)^2 = 1.33 \ (3 \text{ s.f.})$

b The mean and variance are not numerically close so it is unlikely the Poisson will be an adequate model (with only one lane open for traffic, overtaking cannot happen on this stretch of the road and the numbers of cars will be much more consistent than normal – hence the variance is much lower than would be expected if the Poisson model did apply).

S2

Derivation of mean and variance of the Poisson distribution

Let $X \sim \text{Po}(\lambda)$

$$P(X = k) = \frac{e^{-\lambda}\lambda^k}{k!}$$

$$E(X) = \sum_{k=0}^{\infty} k \times \frac{e^{-\lambda}\lambda^k}{k!} = \lambda \times \sum_{k=1}^{\infty} \frac{e^{-\lambda}\lambda^{k-1}}{(k-1)!}$$

$$= \lambda$$

As in the binomial case, cancel k, after discarding the zero case.

$$E(X^2) = \sum_{k=0}^{\infty} k^2 \times \frac{e^{-\lambda}\lambda^k}{k!} = \lambda \times \sum_{k=1}^{\infty} k \times \frac{e^{-\lambda}\lambda^{k-1}}{(k-1)!}$$

$$= \lambda \times \sum_{k=1}^{\infty} (k-1+1) \times \frac{e^{-\lambda}\lambda^{k-1}}{(k-1)!}$$

$$= \lambda^2 \times \sum_{k=2}^{\infty} \frac{e^{-\lambda}\lambda^{k-2}}{(k-2)!} + \lambda \times \sum_{k=1}^{\infty} \frac{e^{-\lambda}\lambda^{k-1}}{(k-1)!}$$

$$= \lambda^2 + \lambda$$

Then $\text{Var}(X) = \lambda^2 + \lambda - \lambda^2 = \lambda$

You are not expected to learn this derivation.

S2

Exercise 2.5

1 If $X \sim \text{Po}(3.2)$ find **a** $E(X)$ **b** $\text{Var}(X)$

2 If $X \sim \text{Po}(49)$ find the mean and standard deviation of X.

3 $X \sim \text{Po}(3.5)$. Find

   a the mean and standard deviation of X

   b $P(X > \mu)$ where $\mu = E(X)$

   c $P(X > \mu + 2\sigma)$, where σ is the standard deviation of X

   d $P(X < \mu - 2\sigma)$.

4 X is the number of telephone calls arriving at an office switchboard in a ten-minute period. X may be modelled by a Poisson distribution with parameter 6. Find

   a the mean and standard deviation of X

   b $P(X > \mu)$, where $\mu = E(X)$

   c $P(X > \mu + 2\sigma)$, where σ is the standard deviation of X

   d $P(X < \mu - 2\sigma)$.

5 What can you gather from your answers to part **d** of questions **3** and **4**?

The Poisson distribution describes the number of occurrences in a fixed period of time or space if the events occur independently of one another, at random and at a constant average rate.

Standard examples of Poisson processes in real life include radioactive emissions, traffic passing a fixed point, telephone calls or letters arriving, and accidents occurring.

EXAMPLE 1

The maternity ward of a hospital wanted to work out how many births would be expected during a night.

The hospital had 3000 deliveries each year so, if these happened randomly around the clock, 1000 deliveries would be expected between the hours of midnight and 8.00 a.m. This is the time when many staff are off duty and it is important to ensure that there will be enough people to cope with the workload on any particular night.

The average number of deliveries per night is $\frac{1000}{365}$, which is 2.74.

From this average rate you can calculate the probability of delivering 0, 1, 2, etc. babies each night using the Poisson distribution. Some probabilities are:

$$P(0) = 2.74^0 \frac{e^{-2.74}}{0!} = 0.065 \quad P(2) = 2.74^2 \frac{e^{-2.74}}{2!} = 0.242$$

$$P(1) = 2.74^1 \frac{e^{-2.74}}{1!} = 0.177 \quad P(3) = 2.74^3 \frac{e^{-2.74}}{3!} = 0.221$$

a On how many nights in the year would 5 or fewer deliveries be expected?

b Over the course of one year, what is the greatest number of deliveries expected in any night?

c Why might the pattern of deliveries *not* follow a Poisson distribution?

a Let X = number of deliveries

$365 \times P(X \leqslant 5) = 343$

b 8

This is the largest value for which the probability is greater than $\frac{1}{365}$.

c If deliveries were not random throughout the 24 hours.

E.g. if a lot of women had elective caesareans done during the day.

Real-life example.
By kind permission of the Mathematics Association.

In the real-life example described in Example 1, deliveries in fact followed the Poisson distribution very closely, and the hospital was able to predict the workload accurately.

Remember the conditions for the Poisson distribution:

1 events occur at random
2 events occur independently of one another
3 the average rate of occurrences remains constant
4 there is zero probability of simultaneous occurrences.

Be careful:
Some change in the underlying conditions may alter the nature of the distribution.
E.g. Traffic observed close to a junction, or where there are lane restrictions and traffic is funnelled into a queue travelling at constant speed.

The underlying conditions may be distorted by interference from other effects.
E.g. If a birthday or Christmas occurs during the period considered then the Poisson conditions would not be reasonable for the arrival of letters.

Randomness or independence may be lost because of a difference in the average rate of occurrences.
E.g. The rate of accidents occurring would be expected to vary somewhat as road conditions vary.

S2

EXAMPLE 2

The number of cyclists passing a village post office during the day can be modelled as a Poisson random variable. On average two cyclists pass by in an hour. What is the probability that

a between 10.00 a.m. and 11.00 a.m.
  i   no cyclist passes
  ii more than 3 cyclists pass

b exactly one cyclist passes while the shop-keeper is on a 20-minute tea-break

c more than 3 cyclists pass in an hour exactly once in a six-hour period?

a In an hour (parts **i** and **ii**) $\lambda = 2$.

  i $P(X = 0) = 0.1353$ (either by using the tables, or by calculating e^{-2}).

  ii $P(X > 3) = 1 - P(X \leqslant 3)$
$$= 1 - 0.8571$$
$$= 0.1429 \text{ (from tables)}$$

Example 2 is continued on the next page.

EXAMPLE 2 (CONT.)

b In a 20-minute period $\left(\frac{1}{3}\text{ of an hour}\right)$,

the mean number of cyclists will be $2 \times \frac{1}{3} = \frac{2}{3}$,
which is not in the tables.

$$P(\text{exactly 1}) = \frac{e^{-\frac{2}{3}}\left(\frac{2}{3}\right)^1}{1!} = 0.342\,(3\text{ s.f.})$$

c The situation is that of a binomial distribution.
There are six 'trials', the number of cyclists in each hour is
independent of the other periods, and the probability of
more than 3 in an hour remains the same for all the six
hour-long periods. Therefore if Y is the number of times
that more than 3 cyclists pass by in an hour exactly once
in a six-hour period $Y \sim B(6, 0.1429)$
$P(Y = 1) = 0.3966$

This cannot be treated as a single Poisson distribution with parameter 12 since it specifies a particular event to be considered in each one-hour time period separately.

Using the probability calculated in part **a ii**.

Exercise 2.6

1 For the following random variables state whether they can be modelled by a Poisson distribution.
If they can, give the value of the parameter λ; if they cannot then explain why.

a The average number of cars per minute passing a point on a road is 12.
The traffic is flowing freely.
X = number of cars which pass in a 15-second period.

b The average number of cars per minute passing a point on a road is 14.
There are roadworks blocking one lane of the road.
X = number of cars which pass in a 30-second period.

c Amelie normally gets letters at an average rate of 1.5 per day.
X = number of letters Amelie gets on 22 December.

d A petrol station which stays open all the time gets an average of 832 customers in a 24-hour time period.
X = number of customers in a quarter of an hour at the petrol station.

e An Accident and Emergency department in a hospital treats 32 patients an hour on average.
X = number of patients treated between 1 a.m. and 2 a.m. on a Sunday morning.

2 For the following situations state what assumptions are needed if a Poisson distribution is to be used to model them, and give the value of λ that would be used.

You are *not* expected to do any calculations.

a On average, defects in a roll of cloth occur at a rate of 0.2 per metre.
How many defects are there in a roll which is 8 m long?

b On average, misprints on a page in a magazine occur once in 2 paragraphs.
How many errors are there in a page with 8 paragraphs?

c A small shop averages 8 customers per hour.
How many customers does it have in 20 minutes?

3 An explorer thinks that the number of mosquito bites he gets when he is in the jungle will follow a Poisson distribution.

The explorer records the number of mosquito bites he gets in the jungle during a number of hour-long periods.
The results are summarised in the table.

Number of bites	0	1	2	3	4	5	6	$\geqslant 7$
Frequency	3	7	9	6	6	3	1	0

a Calculate the mean and variance of the number of bites the explorer gets in an hour in the jungle.

b Do you think the Poisson distribution is a good model for the number of bites the explorer gets in an hour in the jungle?

4 The number of emails Serena gets can be modelled by a Poisson distribution with a mean rate of 1.5 per hour.
What is the probability that

a i Serena gets no emails between 4 p.m. and 5 p.m.?
ii Serena gets more than 2 emails between 4 p.m. and 5 p.m.?
iii Serena gets one email between 6 p.m. and 6.20 p.m.?
iv Serena gets more than 2 emails in an hour exactly twice in a five-hour period.?

b Would it be sensible to use the Poisson distribution to find the probability that Serena gets no emails between 4 a.m. and 5 a.m?
Explain why.

S2

If $X \sim B(n, p)$ with n large and p close to 0 then
$X \sim$ *approximately* $Po(\lambda)$ with $\lambda = np$

If p is close to 0,
then $q = 1 - p$ will be close to 1
and npq will be close to np.

np and npq are the mean and variance of the binomial distribution, and the Poisson has the property that the mean and variance are equal.

Here are four examples where the binomial and Poisson distributions have the same mean:

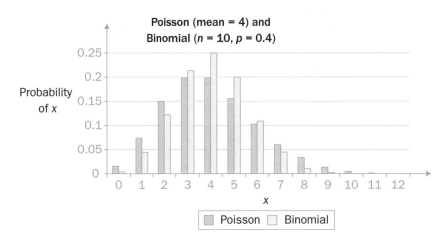

Here the mean of the binomial is 4 and the variance is 2.4.
The two sets of probabilities are not particularly similar.

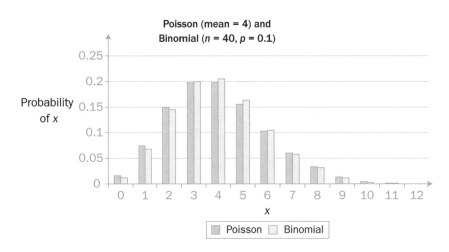

In this case, the variance of the binomial is 3.6. The variance of the Poisson is 4.
The agreement between the two sets of probabilities is quite strong.

S2

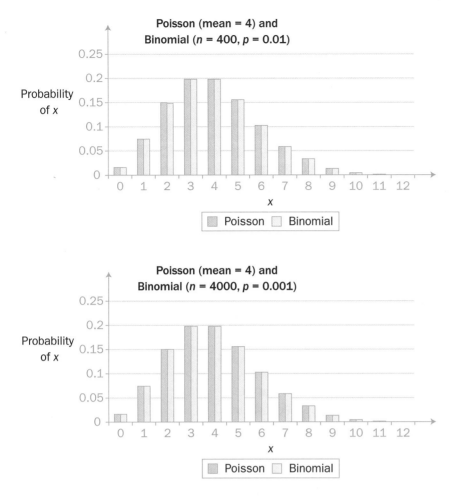

In these two examples, while you cannot see any difference on this scale graphically, there are differences between the binomial and the Poisson in both cases. The differences in the second graph are much smaller than the differences in the first graph.

The use of the Poisson distribution as an approximation to the binomial distribution improves as n increases and as p gets smaller.

The Poisson outcome space has no upper limit whereas the binomial is bounded by the value of n. However, when n is large and p is small, the probabilities of high values of x are very small so this is not a problem.

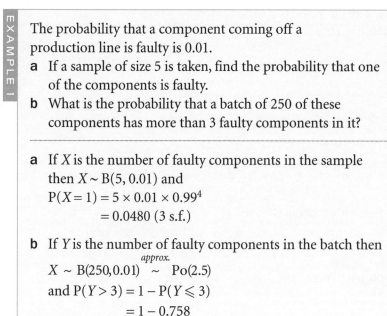

If you are working in a situation where p is close to 1, you can choose to count failures instead of successes and still construct an appropriate Poisson approximation.

Exercise 2.7

1 The proportion of defective pipes coming off a production line is 0.05. A sample of 40 pipes are examined.

   a Using the tables of an exact binomial distribution calculate the probabilities that there are

   i 0   ii 1

   iii 2   iv more than 2

   defectives in the sample.

   b Using an appropriate approximate distribution calculate the probabilities that there are

   i 0   ii 1

   iii 2   iv more than 2

   defectives in the sample.

2 **a** State the conditions under which a Poisson distribution may be used to approximate a binomial distribution.

b 5% of the times a faulty ATM asks for a personal identification number (PIN) it does not register the number entered correctly. If a customer enters their PIN correctly each time, what is the probability that the ATM will not register it correctly in 3 attempts?

c Over a period of time, 90 attempts are made to enter a PIN. If all of the customers enter their PIN correctly, what is the probability that fewer than 3 of the attempts are not registered correctly?

3 In a small town, the football team claims that 95% of the people in town support them. If a survey of 200 randomly chosen people asks whether they support the football team, find the probability that more than 195 people say they do.

4 A rare but harmless medical condition affects 1 in 200 people.

a In a cinema in which 130 people are watching a film, what is the probability that exactly one person has the condition?

b At a concert where the audience is 1800, use an appropriate approximate distribution to find the probability that there are fewer than 5 people with the condition.

5 The Nutty Fruitcase Party claim that 1 in 250 people support their policy to distribute free fruit and nut chocolate bars to children taking examinations.

a In an opinion poll which asks 1000 voters about a range of policies put forward by different parties what is the probability that

    i no one will support the Nutty Fruitcase Party policy
    ii at least 10 people will support the policy.

b If the opinion poll had 7 people supporting the policy, does this mean that the Nutty Fruitcase Party have underestimated the support there is for this policy?

1 Customers enter a shop independently of one another, and at random intervals of time, at an average rate of 5 per hour during the time that the shop is open.

   a If X is the number of customers entering the shop in a one-hour period, write down the distribution that you would use to model X.

   b Use this distribution to calculate the probability that
     i there are 4 customers in one particular hour
     ii there are more than 6 customers in a given hour
     iii there are fewer than 9 customers in a two-hour period
     iv exactly one customer enters in each of four 15-minute periods.

   c Compare the probabilities obtained in parts **i** and **iv** of **b**.

2 Lemons are packed in bags containing 5 each. It is found that, on average, 6% of the lemons are too sour to use.

   a Find the probability that a bag contains
     i one unusable lemon   **ii** more than one unusable lemon.

   b A box containing 15 of these bags is opened and inspected. Identify and use a suitable approximation to find the probability that there are no more than 3 unusable lemons.

3 A shop sells a particular make of DVD player.

   a Assuming that the weekly demand for the DVD player is a Poisson variable with mean 5, find the probability that the shop sells
     i at least 4 in a week
     ii at most 7 in a week
     iii more than 12 in a fortnight (2 weeks).

   b Stocks are brought in only at the beginning of each fortnight. Find the minimum number that should be in stock at the beginning of a fortnight so that the shop can be at least 95% sure of being able to meet all demands during the fortnight.

4 A car hire firm finds that the daily demand for its cars follows a Poisson distribution with mean 4.5.

   a What is the probability that on a particular day the demand is
     i 2 or fewer   **ii** between 4 and 9 (inclusive)   **iii** zero?

   b What is the probability that 8 consecutive days will include two or more on which the demand is zero?

   c Suggest reasons why the daily demand for car hire may not follow a Poisson distribution.

5 Serious accidents in a certain type of manufacturing industry can be adequately modelled by the Poisson distribution with a mean rate of 1.4 per week.

a   What is the probability that there are no serious accidents in a particular week?

b   What is the probability that there are at least three serious accidents in a three-week period?

c   What is the probability that in a four-week period there is exactly one week in which there are serious accidents?

6 A firm is proud of their production statistics, which show that only 0.15% of their components are faulty. The components are packed in boxes of 500.

a   Write down the appropriate exact distribution to model the number of faulty components in a box chosen at random.

i   Give two conditions which need to be satisfied for this distribution to be a suitable model.

ii   Is it reasonable to assume that these conditions would be satisfied?

b   Write down the distribution you would use to calculate the probability that a box contains more than one faulty component.

c   Calculate this probability.

7 A computer repair company uses a particular spare part at a rate of 3 per week. Assuming that requests for this spare part occur at random, find the probability that

a   exactly 4 are used in a particular week

b   at least 10 are used in a two-week period

c   exactly 4 are used in each of three consecutive weeks.

The manager decides to replenish the stock of this spare part to a constant level n at the start of each week.

d   Find the value of n such that, on average, the stock will be insufficient no more than once in a 52 week year.

8 An Internet site is visited on average 5 times an hour during the period between 10 a.m. and 4 p.m., and the visits occur at random intervals of time, independently of one another. What distribution is appropriate to model the numbers of visits recorded between 11 a.m. and 1 p.m? Calculate the probability that there are

a fewer than 4 visits between 11 a.m. and 1 p.m.

b exactly 2 visits between 11 a.m. and 11.30 a.m.

9 a Serious accidents in a large factory can be adequately modelled by the Poisson distribution with a mean rate of 1.3 per month.
  i What is the probability that there are no serious accidents in a particular month?
  ii What is the probability that in a four-month period there is at most one month during which there are serious accidents?

 b i Give *two* assumptions of the Poisson distribution.
  ii Comment on whether you think the Poisson would be the exact distribution for the number of serious accidents in a month.

10 Customers enter a large cafeteria either alone or in groups.

 a The number of customers entering alone between 10.00 a.m. and 11.00 a.m. may be modelled by a Poisson distribution with a mean of 0.6 per minute.

  Find the probability that, during a particular minute between 10.00 a.m. and 11.00 a.m., the number of customers entering the cafeteria alone is
  i 2 or fewer   ii exactly 3.

 b The number of groups of customers entering the cafeteria between 10.00 a.m. and 11.00 a.m. may be modelled by a Poisson distribution with mean of 0.3 per minute. Find the probability that
  i during a particular minute between 10.00 a.m. and 11.00 a.m., more than one group of customers enters the shop
  ii 4 or more groups of customers enter the cafeteria between 10.30 a.m. and 10.45 a.m.

 c Explain whether the Poisson distribution is likely to provide a suitable model for the *number of customers* entering the cafeteria in groups during each minute between 10.00 a.m. and 11.00 a.m.

 d The cafeteria is open from 8.00 a.m. until 6.00 p.m. Explain whether the Poisson distribution is likely to provide a suitable model for the number of customers entering the cafeteria alone during each minute when the cafeteria is open.

11 Rachelle sells a magazine which is produced to raise money for homeless people. The probability of making a sale is 0.05 for each person she approaches.

    a   Given that she approaches 30 people, find the probability that she will make

        i   2 or fewer sales

        ii more than 4 sales.

    b   Find the probability that she makes 2 sales given that she approaches 24 people.

    c   State *one* assumption you have made.

12 The average number of calls to a telephone exchange during the half hour from 10 a.m. to 10.30 a.m. on weekdays is six. Find the probability that

                                               You may assume that the Poisson model is adequate.

    a   on a given weekday between these times, the exchange will receive exactly four calls.

    b   on any given weekday, the exchange will receive more than three calls between 10 a.m. and 10.10 a.m.

13 The number of vehicles arriving at a toll bridge during a 5-minute period can be modelled by a Poisson distribution with mean 2.4.

    a   State the value for the standard deviation of the number of vehicles arriving at the toll bridge during a 5-minute period.

    b   Find the probability that

        i   at least 2 vehicles arrive in a 5-minute period.

        ii at least 2 vehicles arrive in each of three successive 5-minute periods.

    c   Show that the probability that *no* vehicles arrive in a 10 minute period is 0.0082, correct to four decimal places.

S2

2 Exit ⇒

Summary

Refer to

- The Poisson distribution has one parameter, λ.
  - $P(X = r) = \dfrac{e^{-\lambda} \lambda^r}{r!}$ for $r = 0, 1, 2, 3, \ldots$ 2.1
- The Poisson distribution requires certain conditions:
  - events occur at random
  - events occur independently of one another
  - the average rate of occurrences remains constant
  - there is zero probability of simultaneous occurrences.   2.1
  If these conditions are not met completely, the Poisson distribution
  may still provide a reasonable model.   2.6
- The value of the parameter is proportional to the length of the interval
  (of time or space).   2.2
- If $X \sim \text{Po}(\lambda)$ then $P(X = k + 1) = \dfrac{\lambda}{k + 1} \times P(X = k)$ 2.3
- The probability tables for the Poisson distribution give the cumulative
  probability for certain values of λ for values of λ in increments of 0.5 up to 10.   2.4
- If $X \sim \text{Po}(\lambda)$, then $E(X) = \lambda$; $\text{Var}(X) = (\sigma^2) = \lambda$ 2.5
- If $X \sim \text{B}(n, p)$ with n large and p close to 0
  then $X \sim$ *approximately* $\text{Po}(\lambda)$ with $\lambda = np$ 2.7

Links

The Poisson distribution can be used to model a large
number of natural and social phenomena as well as
providing a good approximation to large binomial
distributions under certain conditions.

The number of genetic mutations in a stretch of DNA
may be modeled by the Poisson distribution.

This can help in the understanding of mutations in
both plants and animals and can be applied to medical
research in diseases such as cancer and Parkinson's.

3

Continuous random variables

This chapter will show you how to
- work with the probability density function and the cumulative distribution function for a continuous random variable
- calculate the mean, variance and standard deviation of a continuous random variable
- calculate the mode, median and quartiles of a continuous random variable.

Before you start

You should know how to:

1 Differentiate polynomial functions.

2 Find turning points of a polynomial function.

3 Solve quadratic equations.

4 Integrate polynomial functions.

Check in:

1 If $y = 5x^2 - 2x + 1$
find $\dfrac{dy}{dx}$.

2 Find the turning point of the function given in question **1**.

3 Solve $3x^2 - 8x + 1 = 0$
Give your answers to 2 d.p.

4 Calculate
$$\int_{-1}^{2} (x^2 - 2x + 5)\, dx$$

The times taken by competitors in the swimming section of a triathlon are shown in the following histograms, with smaller and smaller intervals:

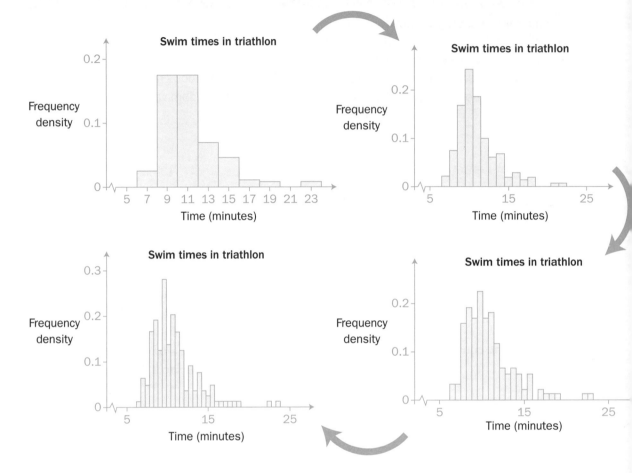

These histograms are drawn as frequency density diagrams, so the total area of all the bars is always 1.

Taking smaller and smaller intervals, the end result would be this smooth curve, which is a good representation of the distribution of times for the competition. On a different day or on a different course, the distribution might be different.

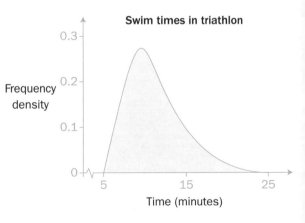

This smooth curve represents a continuous random variable.
It takes on an infinite number of possible values. You can find probabilities from the area under the curve.

Exercise 3.1

1 State which of the following random variables are continuous.

   a The length of the winning throw in the men's javelin competition at the next Olympic Games

   b The number of blades of grass in a 1 square metre area of lawn

   c The volume of water in a bottle

   d The length of time it takes Habib to walk to school on a particular morning

   e The number of times Hayley is late for school in a particular term.

2 These histograms show the durations of eruptions and the time between eruptions of the Old Faithful Geyser in Yellowstone Park.

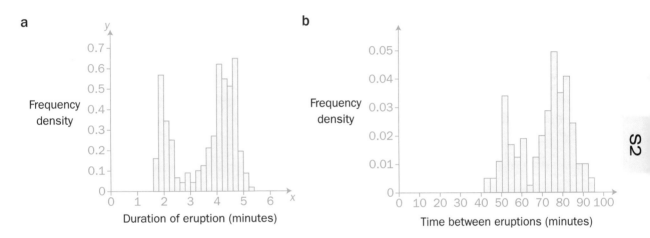

a Duration of eruption (minutes)

b Time between eruptions (minutes)

Sketch what you think the graph of each of the continuous random variables looks like on separate diagrams.

3 The histogram shows the weights in grams of dunnocks (hedge sparrows).

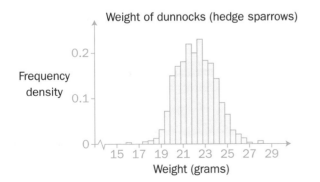

Weight of dunnocks (hedge sparrows)

Weight (grams)

Sketch what you think the graph of the continuous random variable looks like.

S2

3.2 Probability density functions

To calculate probabilities relating to a continuous random variable, you need a continuous function known as a probability density function (pdf).

> To be a probability density function (pdf), $f(x)$ must satisfy these basic properties:
>
> - $f(x) \geqslant 0$ for all x, so that no probabilities are negative
>
> - $\int_{-\infty}^{\infty} f(x)\,dx = 1$; often $f(x)$ is only defined over a small range, in which case the integral over that range will be 1.

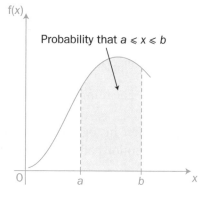

Probability that $a \leqslant x \leqslant b$

You can find the probability that a random variable lies between $x = a$ and $x = b$ from the area under the curve represented by $f(x)$ between those two points.

EXAMPLE 1

a Show that $f(x)$ is a probability density function where

$$f(x) = \begin{cases} \frac{1}{2}(x-3) & \text{for } 3 \leqslant x \leqslant 5 \\ 0 & \text{otherwise} \end{cases}$$

b Find $P(X < 4)$.

> For a continuous random variable there is no difference between $<$ and $\leqslant$ (or between $>$ and $\geqslant$).

....

a $f(x) \geqslant 0$ for all x that the function is defined for.

$$\int_3^5 f(x)\,dx = \int_3^5 \left\{\frac{1}{2}(x-3)\right\}dx = \left[\frac{1}{4}x^2 - \frac{3}{2}x\right]_3^5$$

$$= \left(\frac{25}{4} - \frac{15}{2}\right) - \left(\frac{9}{4} - \frac{9}{2}\right) = 1$$

so $f(x)$ is a probability density function.

b

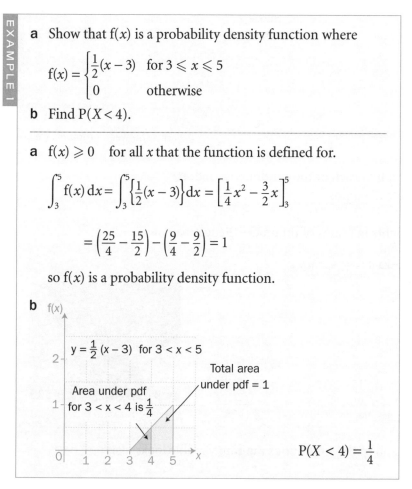

$y = \frac{1}{2}(x-3)$ for $3 < x < 5$

Total area under pdf = 1

Area under pdf for $3 < x < 4$ is $\frac{1}{4}$

$$P(X < 4) = \frac{1}{4}$$

EXAMPLE 2

For the following functions, state whether they could be used as a pdf.
If not explain why.

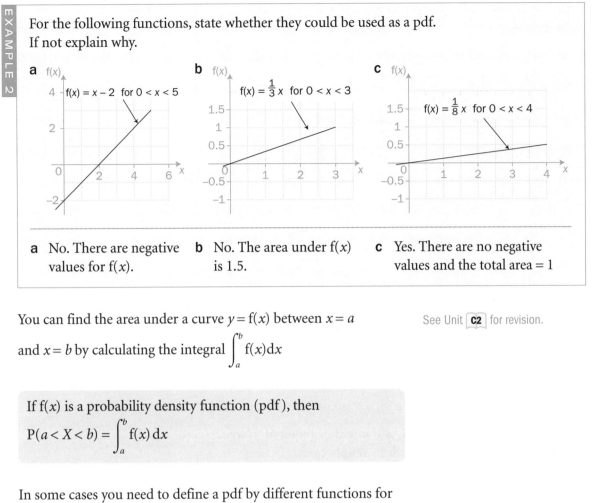

a No. There are negative values for f(x).

b No. The area under f(x) is 1.5.

c Yes. There are no negative values and the total area = 1

You can find the area under a curve $y = f(x)$ between $x = a$
and $x = b$ by calculating the integral $\displaystyle\int_a^b f(x)dx$

See Unit **C2** for revision.

If f(x) is a probability density function (pdf), then

$$P(a < X < b) = \int_a^b f(x)\,dx$$

In some cases you need to define a pdf by different functions for
different values of x.

EXAMPLE 3

$$f(x) = \begin{cases} x & \text{for } 0 \leqslant x \leqslant 1 \\ 2 - x & \text{for } 1 \leqslant x \leqslant 2 \\ 0 & \text{otherwise} \end{cases}$$

gives a pdf with graph as shown.
Find $P(0.5 < X < 1.3)$.

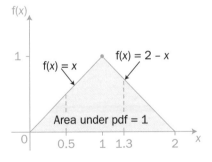

$$P(0.5 < X < 1.3) = \int_{0.5}^{1.3} f(x)\,dx$$

$$= \int_{0.5}^{1} x\,dx + \int_{1}^{1.3} (2 - x)\,dx$$

$$= \left[\tfrac{1}{2}x^2\right]_{0.5}^{1} + \left[2x - \tfrac{1}{2}x^2\right]_{1}^{1.3}$$

$$= \left(\tfrac{1}{2} - \tfrac{1}{8}\right) + \left(\left(2.6 - \tfrac{1.3^2}{2}\right) - \left(2 - \tfrac{1}{2}\right)\right) = 0.63$$

S2

Since the total probability must be 1, a pdf could have a constant in its definition.

S2

EXAMPLE 4

$$f(x) = \begin{cases} k(9 - x^2) & \text{for } -3 \leqslant x \leqslant 3 \\ 0 & \text{otherwise} \end{cases}$$

a Find the value of k and calculate $P(-1 < X < 2)$.

b Find $P(X = 2)$.

a $\displaystyle\int_{-3}^{3} k(9 - x^2)\,dx = k\left[9x - \frac{x^3}{3}\right]_{-3}^{3}$

$$= k((27 - 9) - (-27 - -9)) = 36k \quad \text{so } k = \frac{1}{36}$$

$$P(-1 < X < 2) = \int_{-1}^{2} \frac{1}{36}(9 - x^2)\,dx = \frac{1}{36}\left[9x - \frac{x^3}{3}\right]_{-1}^{2}$$

$$= \frac{1}{36}\left(\left(18 - \frac{8}{3}\right) - \left(-9 - \frac{-1}{3}\right)\right) = \frac{24}{36} = \frac{2}{3}$$

b For a continuous distribution the probability of a single value is 0.

If you are given a sketch of a pdf, you might be required to write down the function form of the pdf in simple cases.

EXAMPLE 5

Express the pdf shown in this sketch as a function.

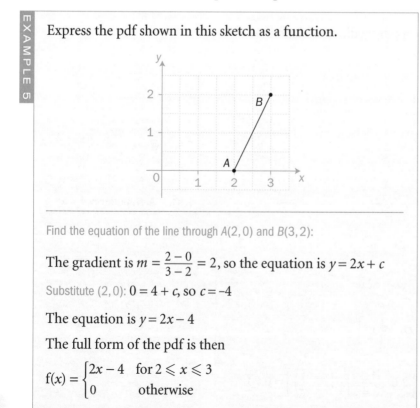

Find the equation of the line through $A(2, 0)$ and $B(3, 2)$:

The gradient is $m = \dfrac{2 - 0}{3 - 2} = 2$, so the equation is $y = 2x + c$

Substitute $(2, 0)$: $0 = 4 + c$, so $c = -4$

The equation is $y = 2x - 4$

The full form of the pdf is then

$$f(x) = \begin{cases} 2x - 4 & \text{for } 2 \leqslant x \leqslant 3 \\ 0 & \text{otherwise} \end{cases}$$

Exercise 3.2

1 Which of the following functions could be probability density functions?

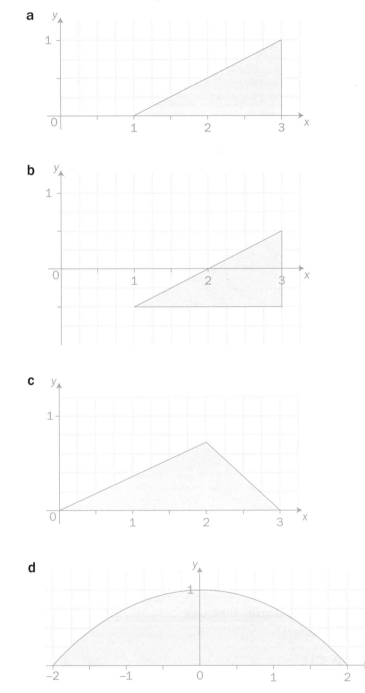

a

b

c

d

2 The graphs of two probability density functions are shown.

a

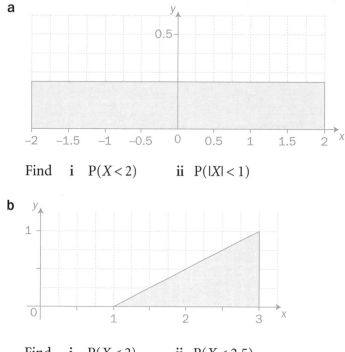

Find   i   P(X < 2)   ii   P(|X| < 1)

b

Find   i   P(X < 2)   ii   P(X < 2.5)

3 Find the value of k for which the following functions can represent a probability density function.
(In each case f(x) is 0 outside the defined range).

a $f(x) = \frac{x}{4}$ $1 \leqslant x \leqslant k$

b $f(x) = kx$ $0 \leqslant x \leqslant 3$

c $f(x) = \frac{x}{6} + k$ $0 \leqslant x \leqslant 3$

d $f(x) = kx^2$ $0 \leqslant x \leqslant 1$

e $f(x) = kx^2$ $-1 \leqslant x \leqslant 1$

4 The following functions represent a probability density function.
(In each case f(x) is 0 outside the defined range).

a $f(x) = \frac{x}{2}$ $0 \leqslant x \leqslant 2$ Find P(X < 1)

b $f(x) = \frac{1}{8}x$ $0 \leqslant x \leqslant 4$ Find P(1 < X < 2)

c $f(x) = \frac{x}{10} + k$ $0 \leqslant x \leqslant 2$ Find k and P(X > 1)

d $f(x) = \frac{3}{8}x^2$ $0 \leqslant x \leqslant 2$ Find   i   P(X < 1)   ii   P(X = 1.5)

e $f(x) = kx^2$ $1 \leqslant x \leqslant 3$ Find k and P(X < 2.5)

5 For each of the following probability density functions, give the equation.

Make sure you define each pdf for all values of x from $-\infty$ to ∞.

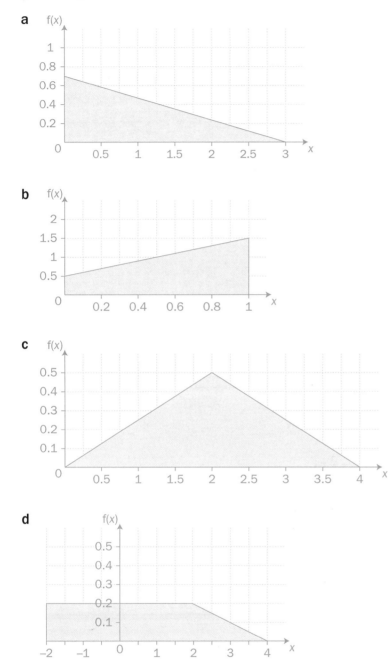

a f(x)

b f(x)

c f(x)

d f(x)

6 For the probability density functions in the corresponding parts of question 5, find

a i $P(X > 2)$ ii $P(X < 0.5)$

b i $P(X > 0.2)$ ii $P(X < 1)$

c i $P(X > 2)$ ii $P(X < 0.3)$ iii $P(X = 1.5)$

d i $P(X > 1)$ ii $P(|X| > 1)$

In S1, the cumulative distribution function (cdf) $F(x_0)$ was defined as $P(X \leqslant x_0)$ for discrete random variables.

For continuous random variables, you can find the cdf by integrating the pdf. Similarly you can find the pdf from the cdf by differentiating.

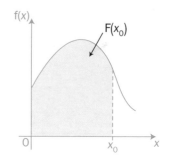

If $f(x)$ is a pdf and $F(x)$ is the corresponding cdf, then

$$f(x) = \frac{d}{dx}(F(x)) \Leftrightarrow F(x_0) = \int_{-\infty}^{x_0} f(x)\,dx$$

where x_0 is a particular value of X.

The cumulative frequency tells you the frequency up to a particular value, x_0. The cdf tells you the probability up to x_0.

EXAMPLE 1

$$f(x) = \begin{cases} \frac{1}{2}(x-3) & \text{for } 3 \leqslant x \leqslant 5 \\ 0 & \text{otherwise} \end{cases}$$

is a pdf.

Find the cumulative distribution function.

$$P(X < x_0) = \int_{-\infty}^{x_0} f(x)\,dx = \int_{3}^{x_0} f(x)\,dx$$

$$= \int_{3}^{x_0} \left\{ \frac{1}{2}(x-3) \right\} dx = \left[\frac{1}{4}x^2 - \frac{3}{2}x \right]_{3}^{x_0}$$

$$= \left(\frac{x_0^2}{4} - \frac{3x_0}{2} \right) + \frac{9}{4}$$

$-\left(\frac{1}{4} \times 3^2 - \frac{3}{2} \times 3 \right) = \frac{9}{4}$

So the cdf is $F(x) = \left(\frac{x^2}{4} - \frac{3x}{2} \right) + \frac{9}{4}$ for $3 \leqslant x \leqslant 5$

and to complete the definition you should state explicitly that

EXAMPLE 2

If $F(x) = \begin{cases} 0 & x \leqslant 0 \\ \frac{1}{9}x^2 & 0 \leqslant x \leqslant 3 \\ 1 & x \geqslant 3 \end{cases}$ find $f(x)$.

$f(x) = \frac{d}{dx}(F(x)) = \frac{d}{dx}\left(\frac{1}{9}x^2 \right) = \frac{2}{9}x$ for $0 \leqslant x \leqslant 3$
and $f(x) = 0$ elsewhere.

S2

Exercise 3.3

1 For each of the following pdfs find the cumulative distribution function, and use it to give the required probability.

In each case f(x) is 0 outside the defined range.

a $f(x) = \dfrac{2x}{9}$ $0 \leqslant x \leqslant 3$ Find $P(X < 1)$

b $f(x) = \dfrac{1}{12}x$ $1 \leqslant x \leqslant 5$ Find $P(1 < X < 2)$

c $f(x) = \dfrac{x}{5} + k$ $0 \leqslant x \leqslant 2$ Find k and $P(X > 1)$

d $f(x) = \dfrac{1}{9}x^2$ $0 \leqslant x \leqslant 3$ Find $P(X < 1.5)$

e $f(x) = k$ $1 \leqslant x \leqslant 3$ Find k and $P(X < 2.5)$

f $f(x) = \dfrac{x}{3}$ $1 \leqslant x \leqslant k$ Find k and $P(X < 2)$

g $f(x) = kx$ $-1 \leqslant x \leqslant 0$ Find k and $P(X > -0.5)$

2 The continuous random variable X has cumulative distribution function given by

$$F(x) = \begin{cases} 0 & x < 0 \\ \dfrac{1}{2}x & 0 \leqslant x \leqslant 2 \\ 1 & x > 2 \end{cases}$$

Find

a $P(X < 1)$ b $P(X > 0.5)$

c $P(0.5 < X < 1.2)$ d the pdf of X.

3 The continuous random variable X has cumulative distribution function given by

$$F(x) = \begin{cases} 0 & x < 1 \\ (x-1)^2 & 1 \leqslant x \leqslant 2 \\ 1 & x > 2 \end{cases}$$

Find

a $P(X < 1.5)$ b $P(X > 0.5)$

c $P(1.2 < X < 1.7)$ d the pdf of X.

4 The continuous random variable X has cumulative distribution function given by

$$F(x) = \begin{cases} 0 & x < 1 \\ \frac{1}{4}(x-1)^2 & 1 \leqslant x \leqslant 3 \\ 1 & x > 3 \end{cases}$$

Find

a $P(X < 1.5)$

b $P(X > 2.5)$

c $P(2.5 < X < 2.7)$

d the pdf of X.

5 The continuous random variable X has cumulative distribution function given by

$$F(x) = \begin{cases} 0 & x < 1 \\ \frac{1}{2}x^2 - x + \frac{1}{2} & 1 \leqslant x \leqslant 2 \\ 3x - \frac{1}{2}x^2 - \frac{7}{2} & 2 \leqslant x \leqslant 3 \\ 1 & x > 3 \end{cases}$$

Find

a $P(X < 1.5)$

b $P(X > 2)$

c $P(1.2 < X < 2.5)$

d the pdf of X.

6 Sketch the graphs of the pdfs in questions **2** to **5**.

7 Find the values of k so that these functions could be valid cumulative distribution functions. In each case, find the pdf and sketch it.

a $F(x) = \begin{cases} 0 & x < 0 \\ \frac{1}{5}x & 0 \leqslant x \leqslant k \\ 1 & x > k \end{cases}$

b $F(x) = \begin{cases} 0 & x < 0 \\ \frac{1}{5}(x^2 + kx) & 0 \leqslant x \leqslant 1 \\ 1 & x > 1 \end{cases}$

c $F(x) = \begin{cases} 0 & x < 0 \\ \frac{1}{10}(x^2 + 3x) & 0 \leqslant x \leqslant k \\ 1 & x > k \end{cases}$

8 Some of these functions are possible cumulative distribution functions and others are not. If the function is a valid cumulative distribution function find the pdf and sketch it, and if it is not a valid cumulative distribution function explain why not.

a $F(x) = \begin{cases} 0 & x < 0 \\ \frac{1}{3}x & 0 \leqslant x \leqslant 3 \\ 1 & x > 3 \end{cases}$

b $F(x) = \begin{cases} 0 & x < 0 \\ \frac{1}{2}(x^2 + 2x) & 0 \leqslant x \leqslant 1 \\ 1 & x > 1 \end{cases}$

c $F(x) = \begin{cases} 0 & x < 0 \\ \frac{1}{28}(x^2 + 3x) & 0 \leqslant x \leqslant 4 \\ 1 & x > 4 \end{cases}$

d $F(x) = \begin{cases} 0 & x < 0 \\ \frac{1}{3}x^2 & 0 \leqslant x \leqslant 1 \\ x - \frac{1}{6}x^2 - \frac{1}{2} & 1 \leqslant x \leqslant 3 \\ 1 & x > 3 \end{cases}$

e $F(x) = \begin{cases} 0 & x < 0 \\ \frac{1}{2}x^2 & 0 \leqslant x \leqslant 1 \\ \frac{1}{2}(x^2 - x) & 1 \leqslant x \leqslant 2 \\ 1 & x > 2 \end{cases}$

9 X is the continuous random variable with pdf given by

$f(x) = \begin{cases} \frac{1}{2} & \text{for } 0 \leqslant x \leqslant 2 \\ 0 & \text{otherwise} \end{cases}$

This question goes beyond the S2 specification, but shows one of the most powerful applications of the cumulative distribution function.

a Show that the cumulative distribution function is

$F(x) = \begin{cases} 0 & x < 0 \\ \frac{1}{2}x & 0 \leqslant x \leqslant 2 \\ 1 & x > 2 \end{cases}$

b Three observations X_1, X_2 and X_3 are taken and the new random variable Y is defined to be the maximum of X_1, X_2 and X_3.

Show that the cumulative distribution function of Y is given by

$F(y) = \begin{cases} 0 & y < 0 \\ \left(\frac{1}{2}y\right)^3 & 0 \leqslant y \leqslant 2 \\ 1 & y > 2 \end{cases}$

c Find the pdf of the random variable Y.

The **mean** or **expected value** of a discrete probability distribution is defined as

See **S1** for revision.

$$\mu = E(X) = \sum px$$

For a continuous random variable

$$\mu = E(X) = \int_{-\infty}^{\infty} xf(x)\,dx$$

where in practice the limits will be the limits of the interval over which f(x) is defined.

The probability density function f(x) has replaced p and the summation has become an integral.

EXAMPLE 1

$$f(x) = \begin{cases} \frac{1}{2}(x-3) & \text{for } 3 \leqslant x \leqslant 5 \\ 0 & \text{otherwise} \end{cases}$$

Find E(X).

This is f(x) from Example 1 in Section 3.2.

Use the formula:

$$\mu = E(X) = \int_{-\infty}^{\infty} xf(x)\,dx$$

$$= \int_{3}^{5} \left\{ x\frac{1}{2}(x-3) \right\} dx$$

$$= \int_{3}^{5} \left\{ \frac{x^2}{2} - \frac{3x}{2} \right\} dx$$

$$= \left[\frac{1}{6}x^3 - \frac{3}{4}x^2 \right]_{3}^{5}$$

$$= \left(\frac{125}{6} - \frac{75}{4} \right) - \left(\frac{27}{6} - \frac{27}{4} \right) = \frac{13}{3}$$

Recall the definition of **variance**:
$$\text{Var}(X) = \sigma^2 = E[\{X - E(X)\}^2]$$

You almost always use the computational form
$$\sigma^2 = E(X^2) - \mu^2 \text{ where } \mu = E(X)$$

For a continuous random variable $E(X^2) = \int_{-\infty}^{\infty} x^2 f(x)\,dx$

S2

EXAMPLE 2

Find the standard deviation for the pdf in Example 1.

$$E(X^2) = \int_{-\infty}^{\infty} x^2 f(x)\, dx$$

$$= \int_3^5 \left\{ x^2 \frac{1}{2}(x-3) \right\} dx$$

$$= \int_3^5 \left\{ \frac{x^3}{2} - \frac{3x^2}{2} \right\} dx$$

$$= \left[\frac{1}{8}x^4 - \frac{1}{2}x^3 \right]_3^5$$

$$= \left(\frac{625}{8} - \frac{125}{2} \right) - \left(\frac{81}{8} - \frac{27}{2} \right) = 19$$

and $\sigma^2 = E(X^2) - \mu^2 = 19 - \left(\frac{13}{3} \right)^2 = \frac{2}{9}$

so the standard deviation of X is $\sqrt{\frac{2}{9}} = 0.471$ (3 s.f.)

> The standard deviation is the square root of the variance.

EXAMPLE 3

The continuous random variable X has probability density function

$$f(x) = \begin{cases} kx & 0 \leqslant x \leqslant 5 \\ 0 & \text{otherwise} \end{cases}$$

a Find the value of k.

b Find the mean and variance of X.

c Calculate
  i $P(X > \mu)$ and
  ii $P(X > \mu + \sigma)$ where μ is the mean and σ is the standard deviation of X.

a $F(x) = \begin{cases} 0 & x < 0 \\ \frac{k}{2}x^2 & 0 \leqslant x \leqslant 5 \\ 1 & x > 5 \end{cases}$ so $\frac{k}{2} \times 5^2 = 1 \Rightarrow k = \frac{2}{25}$

b $\mu = E(X) = \int_{-\infty}^{\infty} xf(x)\, dx$

$$= \int_0^5 \left\{ x \frac{2}{25} x \right\} dx$$

$$= \int_0^5 \left\{ \frac{2}{25} x^2 \right\} dx = \left[\frac{2}{75} x^3 \right]_0^5 = \frac{2 \times 125}{75} - 0 = \frac{10}{3}$$

Example 3 is continued on the next page.

EXAMPLE 3 (CONT.)

$$E(X^2) = \int_{-\infty}^{\infty} x^2 f(x)\, dx$$

$$= \int_0^5 \left(x \frac{2}{25} x^2 \right) dx$$

$$= \int_0^5 \left(\frac{2}{25} x^3 \right) dx$$

$$= \left[\frac{1}{50} x^4 \right]_0^5 = \frac{625}{50} - 0 = 12.5$$

and $\sigma^2 = E(X^2) - \mu^2 = 12.5 - \left(\frac{10}{3} \right)^2 = \frac{25}{18}$

c   i $P(X > \mu) = 1 - F\left(\frac{10}{3} \right) = 1 - \frac{1}{25}\left(\frac{10}{3} \right)^2 = \frac{5}{9}$

   ii $P(X > \mu + \sigma) = 1 - F\left(\frac{10}{3} + \sqrt{\left(\frac{25}{18} \right)} \right)$

$$= 1 - \frac{1}{25}\left(\frac{10}{3} + \sqrt{\left(\frac{25}{18} \right)} \right)^2 = 0.186 \ (3 \text{ s.f.})$$

You can work out a decimal value for $\mu + \sigma$ but you need to keep enough decimal places in it to give answers to 3 s.f. The best way of doing this is to calculate $\mu + \sigma = 4.5118 \ldots$ and make this the last calculation done on your calculator, then the *exact* value can be used by pressing the (Ans) key.

EXAMPLE 4

The continuous random variable Y has probability density function.

$$f(y) = \begin{cases} y & \text{for } 0 \leqslant y \leqslant 1 \\ 2 - y & \text{for } 1 \leqslant y \leqslant 2 \\ 0 & \text{otherwise} \end{cases}$$

Find the mean and variance of Y.

The pdf looks like this, so the mean must 1 by symmetry. The derivation is shown formally to show the procedure.

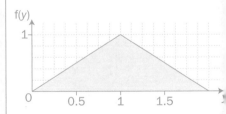

a $\mu = E(Y) = \int_{-\infty}^{\infty} y f(y)\, dy$

$$= \int_0^1 \{ y \times y \}\, dy + \int_1^2 \{ y(2 - y) \}\, dy$$

$$= \int_0^1 \{ y^2 \}\, dy + \int_1^2 \{ (2y - y^2) \}\, dy$$

$$= \left[\frac{1}{3} y^3 \right]_0^1 + \left[y^2 - \frac{1}{3} y^3 \right]_1^2$$

$$= \left[\frac{1}{3} - 0 \right] + \left[\left[4 - \frac{8}{3} \right] - \left[1 - \frac{1}{3} \right] \right] = 1$$

EXAMPLE 4 (CONT.)

$$E(Y^2) = \int_{-\infty}^{\infty} y^2 f(y)\, dy$$

$$= \int_0^1 \{y^2 \times y\}\, dy + \int_1^2 \{y^2 \times (2-y)\}\, dy$$

$$= \int_0^1 \{y^3\}\, dy + \int_1^2 (2y^2 - y^3)\, dy$$

$$= \left[\frac{1}{4}y^4\right]_0^1 + \left[\frac{2}{3}y^3 - \frac{1}{4}y^4\right]_1^2$$

$$= \left(\frac{1}{4} - 0\right) + \left[\left(\frac{16}{3} - 4\right) - \left(\frac{2}{3} - \frac{1}{4}\right)\right] = \frac{7}{6}$$

and $\sigma^2 = E(Y^2) - \mu^2 = \frac{7}{6} - 1^2 = \frac{1}{6}$

EXAMPLE 5

The continuous random variable X has probability density function

$$f(x) = \begin{cases} \dfrac{1}{36}(9 - x^2) & \text{for } -3 \leqslant x \leqslant 3 \\ 0 & \text{otherwise} \end{cases}$$

a Find the mean and variance of X.

b Calculate
  i $P(X > 2)$ and
  ii $P(|X| > \sigma)$ where σ is the standard deviation of X.

a $\mu = E(X) = \displaystyle\int_{-\infty}^{\infty} x f(x)\, dx$

$$= \int_{-3}^3 \left(x \times \frac{1}{36}(9 - x^2)\right) dx$$

$$= \int_{-3}^3 \left(\frac{1}{36}(9x - x^3)\right) dx$$

$$= \left[\frac{1}{36}\left(\frac{9}{2}x^2 - \frac{x^4}{4}\right)\right]_{-3}^3$$

$$= \frac{1}{36}\left\{\left(\frac{81}{2} - \frac{81}{4}\right) - \left(\frac{81}{2} - \frac{81}{4}\right)\right\} = 0$$

You could find this using the symmetry of the pdf.

$$E(X^2) = \int_{-\infty}^{\infty} x^2 f(x)\, dx$$

$$= \int_{-3}^3 \left(x^2 \times \frac{1}{36}(9 - x^2)\right) dx$$

$$= \int_{-3}^3 \left(\frac{1}{36}(9x^2 - x^4)\right) dx$$

$$= \left[\frac{1}{36}\left(3x^3 - \frac{x^5}{5}\right)\right]_{-3}^3$$

$$= \frac{1}{36}\left\{\left(81 - \frac{243}{5}\right) - \left(-81 - \frac{-243}{5}\right)\right\} = 1.8$$

and $\sigma^2 = E(X^2) - \mu^2 = 1.8(-0^2) = 1.8$

S2

EXAMPLE 5 (CONT.)

b i $P(X > 2) = \int_2^\infty f(x)dx = \int_2^3 \left(\frac{1}{36}(9 - x^2)\right)dx$

$$= \frac{1}{36}\left[9x - \frac{x^3}{3}\right]_2^3$$

$$= \frac{1}{36}\left[(27 - 9) - \left(18 - \frac{8}{3}\right)\right] = \frac{2}{27}$$

ii $P(|X| > \sigma)$ will be $2 \times P(X > \sigma)$ by symmetry, and $\sigma = \sqrt{1.8}$ from part **a**.

$$P(X > \sigma) = \int_{\sqrt{1.8}}^3 f(x)\,dx = \int_{\sqrt{1.8}}^3 \left\{\frac{1}{36}(9 - x^2)\right\}dx$$

$$= \frac{1}{36}\left[9x - \frac{x^3}{3}\right]_{\sqrt{1.8}}^3$$

$$= \frac{1}{36}\left[(27 - 9) - \left(9\sqrt{1.8} - \frac{(\sqrt{1.8})^3}{3}\right)\right] = 0.18695...$$

$$P(|X| > \sigma) = 0.374 \text{ (3 s.f.)}$$

EXAMPLE 6

The weekly petrol consumption, in hundreds of litres, of a sales representative may be modelled by the random variable X with probability density function

$$f(x) = \begin{cases} ax^2(b - x) & \text{for } 0 \leqslant x \leqslant 2 \\ 0 & \text{otherwise} \end{cases}$$

a Find the values of a and b if the mean consumption is 144 litres.

b Find the standard deviation of the weekly petrol consumption.

....

The total probability is 1, so $1 = \int_{-\infty}^\infty f(x)dx$

$$1 = \int_0^2 ax^2(b - x)\,dx = \left[\frac{ab}{3}x^3 - \frac{a}{4}x^4\right]_0^2$$

$$= \left(\frac{8ab}{3} - 4a\right) - 0 \quad \text{so } 8ab - 12a = 3 \qquad (1)$$

a $\mu = E(X) = \int_{-\infty}^\infty xf(x)\,dx$

$$= \int_0^2 \{xax^2(b - x)\}\,dx = \int_0^2 \{abx^3 - ax^4\}\,dx$$

$$= \left[\frac{ab}{4}x^4 - \frac{a}{5}x^5\right]_0^2 = \left(4ab - \frac{32a}{5}\right) - 0 = 1.44$$

so $20ab - 32a = 7.2$ $\qquad$ (2)

Solving equations (1) and (2) gives $a = \frac{3}{20}$ and $b = 4$

EXAMPLE 6 (CONT.)

b $E(X^2) = \int_{-\infty}^{\infty} x^2 f(x)\, dx$

$$= \int_0^2 \left\{ x^2 \frac{3}{20} x^2 (4 - x) \right\} dx$$

$$= \int_0^2 \left\{ \frac{6}{10} x^4 - \frac{3}{20} x^5 \right\} dx$$

$$= \left[\frac{3}{25} x^5 - \frac{1}{40} x^6 \right]_0^2 = \left[\frac{96}{25} - \frac{64}{40} \right] - 0 = \frac{56}{25}$$

So the standard deviation of $X = \sqrt{\dfrac{56}{25} - 1.44^2} = 0.41$

and the standard deviation of the petrol consumption is 41 litres.

Exercise 3.4

1 A probability density function is given by

$$f(x) = \begin{cases} \dfrac{2x}{9} & \text{for } 4 \leqslant x \leqslant 5 \\ 0 & \text{otherwise} \end{cases}$$

Find the mean and variance of X.

2 The continuous random variable X has probability density function

$$f(x) = \begin{cases} kx & \text{for } 0 \leqslant x \leqslant 3 \\ 0 & \text{otherwise} \end{cases}$$

a Find the value of k.

b Find the mean and variance of X.

c Calculate
   i $P(X > \mu)$ and
   ii $P(X > \mu + \sigma)$ where μ is the mean and σ is the standard deviation of X.

3 The continuous random variable X has probability density function

$$f(x) = \begin{cases} 0 & \text{for } x < 0 \\ \dfrac{1}{4} x & \text{for } 0 \leqslant x \leqslant 2 \\ \dfrac{1}{4}(4 - x) & \text{for } 2 \leqslant x \leqslant 4 \\ 0 & \text{for } x > 4 \end{cases}$$

Find the mean and variance of X.

S2

4 The continuous random variable X has probability density function

$$f(x) = \begin{cases} kx^3 & \text{for } 0 \leqslant x \leqslant 5 \\ 0 & \text{otherwise} \end{cases}$$

a Find the value of k. **b** Find the mean and variance of X.

c Calculate
  i $P(X > \mu)$ and
  ii $P(X > \mu - 2\sigma)$ where μ is the mean and σ is the standard deviation of X.

5 The continuous random variable X has probability density function

$$f(x) = \begin{cases} kx^4 & \text{for } 0 \leqslant x \leqslant 1 \\ 0 & \text{otherwise} \end{cases}$$

a Find the value of k. **b** Find the mean and variance of X.

c Calculate
  i $P(X < \mu)$ and
  ii $P(|X - \mu| < \sigma)$ where μ is the mean and σ is the standard deviation of X.

6 The length, in metres, of jumps that Carl makes may be modelled by the probability density function

$$f(x) = \begin{cases} k(x - 6)^2 & \text{for } 5.5 \leqslant x \leqslant 6.5 \\ 0 & \text{otherwise} \end{cases}$$

Find

a the value of $E(X)$ **b** the value of k **c** the variance of X.

7 Buses arrive regularly at a bus stop every 15 minutes.

a Gupta does not know the bus schedule so he arrives at the bus stop at random times.
  i If X is the length of time, in minutes, that Gupta has to wait for a bus, explain why

$$f(x) = \begin{cases} \dfrac{1}{15} & \text{for } 0 \leqslant x \leqslant 15 \\ 0 & \text{otherwise} \end{cases}$$

  is a sensible model for the distribution.
  ii Find the mean and variance of X.

b Shirma does know the bus schedule and aims to arrive shortly before a bus is due. If Y is the length of time, in minutes, that Shirma has to wait for a bus, and Y has probability density function given by

$$f(y) = \begin{cases} k(y - 3) & \text{for } 0 \leqslant x \leqslant 3 \\ 0 & \text{otherwise} \end{cases}$$

  i find the value of k **ii** find the mean and variance of Y.

8 The profit, X, in £000s, made on a speculative investment may be modelled by the probability density function given by

$$f(x) = \begin{cases} k(9 + 8x - x^2) & \text{for } -1 \leqslant x \leqslant 4 \\ 0 & \text{otherwise} \end{cases}$$

a Show that $k = \dfrac{3}{250}$

b Find the mean and standard deviation of the profit made on the investment.

c Show that the probability of making a loss on the investment is $\dfrac{7}{125}$.

There is an alternative investment on offer with a guaranteed return of £1500.

d Find the probability that the speculative investment gives a better return.

9 The diameters, in mm, of chips made in car paintwork by flying stones during resurfacing of a road may be modelled by the random variable X with probability density function

$$f(x) = \begin{cases} ax^2(b - x) & \text{for } 0 \leqslant x \leqslant 3 \\ 0 & \text{otherwise} \end{cases}$$

a Show that $a = \dfrac{4}{27}$ and $b = 3$ if the mean diameter is 1.8 mm.

b Find the standard deviation of the diameters.

c Comment on whether you think the pdf given is likely to be a good model to describe the diameters.

S2

The mode of a continuous random variable is the value of x for which f(x) is a maximum over the interval in which f(x) exists.

This is either a stationary point, at which f$'(x) = 0$,
or the end value of the interval over which f(x) is defined.

> There may not be a mode if no single value occurs more often than any other. ('Bimodal' distributions occur commonly in real life).

EXAMPLE 1

$$f(x) = \begin{cases} \frac{1}{36}(9 - x^2) & \text{for } -3 \leqslant x \leqslant 3 \\ 0 & \text{otherwise} \end{cases}$$

Find the mode.

Sketch the pdf:

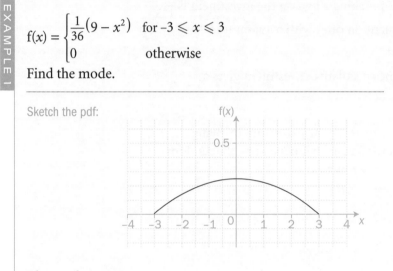

The mode is at 0.

Alternatively you could use differentiation:

$$f(x) = \frac{1}{36}(9 - x^2) \Rightarrow f'(x) = \frac{-2x}{36} = 0 \quad \text{when } x = 0$$

EXAMPLE 2

Find the mode of the pdf from Example 1 in Section 3.2,

$$f(x) = \begin{cases} \frac{1}{2}(x - 3) & \text{for } 3 \leqslant x \leqslant 5 \\ 0 & \text{otherwise} \end{cases}$$

Sketch the graph:

f(x)

f$(x) = \frac{1}{2}(x - 3)$ for $3 < x < 5$

> The differential of f(x) here is just $\frac{1}{2}$, which has no dependence on x, so there will be no stationary value of f$'(x)$. This does not mean there is no mode.

The pdf increases steadily throughout the interval in which it is defined. The mode for the random variable is 5 (the upper bound of the interval in which f(x) is defined).

S2

You can use the cumulative distribution function to find the median and quartiles for a continuous random variable:

If m is the median then $F(m) = 0.5$
If Q_1 is the lower quartile then $F(Q_1) = 0.25$
If Q_3 is the upper quartile then $F(Q_3) = 0.75$

See S1 for revision of the median and quartiles for a frequency distribution.

You can set up an appropriate algebraic equation and solve it to find the required quartile, or decile, or percentile.

E.g. To find the 7th decile solve $F(x) = 0.7$

EXAMPLE 3

$$f(x) = \begin{cases} \frac{1}{2}(x - 3) & \text{for } 3 \leqslant x \leqslant 5 \\ 0 & \text{otherwise} \end{cases}$$

Find

a the median
b the lower and upper quartiles for X.

a The cdf is $F(x) = \left(\frac{x^2}{4} - \frac{3x}{2}\right) + \frac{9}{4}$ for $3 \leqslant x \leqslant 5$

$F(x) = 0$ for $x < 3$
$F(x) = 1$ for $x > 5$

$$S2$$

Use $F(m) = 0.5$ to find the median:

$$F(m) = 0.5 \Rightarrow \left(\frac{m^2}{4} - \frac{3m}{2}\right) + \frac{9}{4} = 0.5$$

$$m^2 - 6m + 7 = 0$$

$$\Rightarrow m = \frac{6 + \sqrt{(-6)^2 - 4 \times 1 \times 7}}{2 \times 1}$$

Using the quadratic formula

So $m = 1.58$ or $m = 4.41$

1.58 is not in the required interval.

Median $= 4.41$ to 3 s.f.

b $F(Q_1) = 0.25 \Rightarrow \left(\frac{Q_1^2}{4} - \frac{3Q_1}{2}\right) + \frac{9}{4} = 0.25$

$Q_1^2 - 6Q_1 + 8 = 0 \Rightarrow (Q_1 - 2)(Q_1 - 4) = 0$

2 is not in the required interval.

so $Q_1 = 4$

$F(Q_3) = 0.75 \Rightarrow \left(\frac{Q_3^2}{4} - \frac{3Q_3}{2}\right) + \frac{9}{4} = 0.75$

$$Q_3^2 - 6Q_3 + 6 = 0 \Rightarrow Q_3 = \frac{6 \pm \sqrt{(-6)^2 - 4 \times 1 \times 6}}{2 \times 1}$$

$$= 1.27 \text{ or } 4.73$$

1.27 is not in the required interval.

so $Q_3 = 4.73$

Exercise 3.5

1 The continuous random variable X has cumulative distribution function given by

$$F(x) = \begin{cases} 0 & x < 0 \\ \dfrac{1}{81}x^4 & 0 \leqslant x \leqslant 3 \\ 1 & x > 3 \end{cases}$$

a Find **i** $F(1)$ **ii** $F(2)$

b Show that the median of X is $\sqrt[4]{\dfrac{81}{2}}$

c Find the lower quartile of X.

2 The continuous random variable X has probability density function

given by $f(x) = \begin{cases} \dfrac{3}{2}(x-1)^2 & \text{for } 0 \leqslant x \leqslant 2 \\ 0 & \text{otherwise} \end{cases}$

a Sketch the probability density function.

b State the value of **i** the mode of X **ii** the median of X.

3 The continuous random variable X has cumulative distribution function given by

$$F(x) = \begin{cases} 0 & x < 1 \\ (x-1)^2 & 1 \leqslant x \leqslant 2 \\ 1 & x > 2 \end{cases}$$

a Find the median of X. **b** Find the lower quartile of X. The pdf is $f(x) = 2(x-1)$ where it is not zero.

c Find the mode of X.

4 The continuous random variable X has cumulative distribution function given by

$$F(x) = \begin{cases} 0 & x < 3 \\ \dfrac{1}{4}(x-3)^2 & 3 \leqslant x \leqslant 5 \\ 1 & x > 5 \end{cases}$$

Find **a** the median of X **b** the lower quartile of X.

5 For the random variables with the following probability density functions, find **i** the median **ii** the upper quartile **iii** the mode.

a $f(x) = \dfrac{1}{12}x$ $1 \leqslant x \leqslant 5$ **b** $f(x) = \dfrac{1}{9}x^2$ $0 \leqslant x \leqslant 3$ You can assume that the value of each pdf is zero for x-values outside of the given range.

c $f(x) = \dfrac{x}{2}$ $0 \leqslant x \leqslant 2$ **d** $f(x) = \dfrac{3}{8}x^2$ $0 \leqslant x \leqslant 2$

6 The continuous random variable X has cumulative distribution function given by

$$F(x) = \begin{cases} 0 & x < 0 \\ \dfrac{1}{16}(x^3 + 4x) & 0 \leqslant x \leqslant 2 \\ 1 & x > 2 \end{cases}$$

Verify that the median lies between 1.36 and 1.37.

7 The continuous random variable X has pdf given by

$$f(x) = \begin{cases} kx(10 - x) & \text{for } 0 \leqslant x \leqslant 7 \\ 0 & \text{otherwise} \end{cases}$$

Find   a   the value of k b   the mode X.

8 The continuous random variable X has pdf given by

$$f(x) = \begin{cases} \dfrac{1}{8}(4 - x) & \text{for } 0 \leqslant x \leqslant 4 \\ 0 & \text{otherwise} \end{cases}$$

a   Sketch the probability density function.

b   State the value of the mode.

c   Find the median of X.

d   Find the 3rd decile of X.

9 The continuous random variable X has cumulative distribution function given by

$$F(x) = \begin{cases} 0 & x < 2 \\ \dfrac{1}{19}x^3 - \dfrac{8}{19} & 2 \leqslant x \leqslant 3 \\ 1 & x > 3 \end{cases}$$

a   Find the probability density function and sketch it.

b   Find the mode.

c   Show that the median of X lies between 2.5 and 2.6.

10 The continuous random variable X has cumulative distribution function given by

$$F(x) = \begin{cases} 0 & x < 0 \\ \dfrac{-1}{27}x^3 + \dfrac{2}{9}x^2 & 0 \leqslant x \leqslant 3 \\ 1 & x > 3 \end{cases}$$

a   Find the probability density function and sketch it.

b   Find the mode.

c   Show that the median of X lies between 1.7 and 1.8.

S2

1 A continuous random variable X has a probability density function of the form

$$f(x) = \begin{cases} A(x^2 + 4) & \text{for } 0 \leqslant x \leqslant 1 \\ 0 & \text{otherwise} \end{cases}$$

  a   Calculate the value of A.

  b   Find $P\left(\frac{1}{2} \leqslant x \leqslant 1\right)$ correct to 2 decimal places.

  c   Calculate $E(X)$ and $Var(X)$.

2 A continuous random variable X has a pdf of the form

$$f(x) = \begin{cases} \dfrac{x}{6} + C & \text{for } 0 \leqslant x \leqslant 3 \\ 0 & \text{otherwise} \end{cases}$$

  a   Calculate the value of C.

  b   Find $P(1 \leqslant x \leqslant 2)$.

  c   Calculate $E(X)$ and $Var(X)$.

3 A continuous random variable X has a pdf of the form

$$f(x) = \begin{cases} 1 - \dfrac{x}{2} & \text{for } 0 \leqslant x \leqslant 2 \\ 0 & \text{otherwise} \end{cases}$$

  a   Find the cumulative distribution function $F(x)$.

  b   Find $P(1 \leqslant x \leqslant 2)$.

  c   Calculate $E(X)$ and $Var(X)$.

  d   Calculate $P(X \leqslant \mu)$ where $\mu = E(X)$.

4 A factory produces discs to operate fruit machines. The slots in the fruit machines are 3 cm long and the factory is requested to make discs whose diameters are no more than 2.9 cm and no less than 2.7 cm. The probability density function of X, the disc diameter, is

$$f(x) = \begin{cases} \dfrac{3000}{32}(3.1 - x)(x - 2.7) & 2.7 \leqslant x \leqslant 3.1 \\ 0 & \text{otherwise} \end{cases}$$

  A disc is chosen at random. Find the probability that

  a   the disc does not meet the required specification

  b   the disc does not meet the required specification, but will still fit in the slot.

5 A random variable has a cumulative distribution function given by

$$F(x) = \begin{cases} 0 & x < 0 \\ 3x^2 - 2x^3 & 0 \leqslant x \leqslant 1 \\ 1 & x > 1 \end{cases}$$

Find

a the probability density function $f(x)$

b the mean and variance of X.

6 A teacher of young children is thinking of asking her class to guess her height in metres. The teacher considers that the height guessed by a randomly selected child can be modelled by the random variable H with probability density function

$$f(h) = \begin{cases} \dfrac{3}{16}(4h - h^2) & 0 \leqslant h \leqslant 2 \\ 0 & \text{otherwise} \end{cases}$$

Using this model

a find $P(H < 1)$

b show that $E(H) = 1.25$

A friend of the teacher suggests that the random variable X with probability density function

$$g(x) = \begin{cases} kx^3 & 0 \leqslant x \leqslant 2 \\ 0 & \text{otherwise} \end{cases}$$

where k is a constant, might be a more suitable model.

c Show that $k = \dfrac{1}{4}$

d Find $P(X < 1)$.

e Find $E(X)$.

f Using your calculations in **a, b, c, d** and **e**, state, giving reasons, which of the random variables H or X is likely to be the more appropriate model in this instance.

S2

7 The total number of radio taxi calls received at a control centre in a month is modelled by a random variable X (in tens of thousands of calls) having the probability density function

$$f(x) = \begin{cases} cx & 0 < x < 1 \\ c(2 - x) & 1 \leqslant x < 2 \\ 0 & \text{otherwise} \end{cases}$$

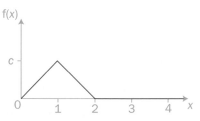

a Show that the value of c is 1.

b Write down the probability that $X \leqslant 1$.

c Show that the cumulative distribution function of X is

$$F(x) = \begin{cases} 0 & x < 0 \\ \dfrac{1}{2}x^2 & 0 \leqslant x < 1 \\ 2x - \dfrac{1}{2}x^2 - 1 & 1 \leqslant x < 2 \\ 1 & x \geqslant 2 \end{cases}$$

d Find the probability that the control centre receives between 8000 and 12 000 calls in a month.

A colleague criticises the model on the grounds that the number of radio calls must be discrete while the model used for X is continuous.

e State briefly whether you consider that it was reasonable to use this model for X.

f Give two reasons why the probability density function in part **a** might be unsuitable as a model.

g Sketch the shape of a more suitable probability density function.

8 At a supermarket, the time, T minutes, that customers have to wait in order to get to the checkout has the probability density function

$$f(t) = \begin{cases} \dfrac{t^2}{18} & 0 \leqslant t < 3 \\ \dfrac{1}{4}(5 - t) & 3 \leqslant t \leqslant 5 \\ 0 & \text{otherwise} \end{cases}$$

a Write down the value of $P(T = 2.5)$.

b Show that the median waiting time is 3 minutes.

c Find the probability that customers have to wait for less than 2 minutes in order to get to the checkout.

d Calculate the mean time that customers have to wait in order to get to the checkout.

9 Every weekday Carmen waits for a bus to go to work. Buses arrive every 7 minutes. She tries to time her arrival at the bus stop with the scheduled arrival of the bus. She does not always get it right, so the time, X, she has to wait is a random variable, with probability density function as shown.

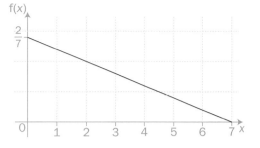

a Prove the probability density function is defined by

$$f(x) = \begin{cases} \dfrac{2}{7} - \dfrac{2}{49}x & \text{for } 0 \leqslant x \leqslant 7 \\ 0 & \text{otherwise} \end{cases}$$

b Find the probability that (on a particular day) she waits more than 4 minutes.

c Show that her expected waiting time is $2\frac{1}{3}$ minutes.

d Calculate the variance of the time she waits.

e Comment on the suitability of this model.

10 A class did a test. The distribution of times in minutes, t, that the students took to finish the test is given by the probability density function

$$f(t) = \begin{cases} -0.006t^2 + 0.42t - 7.2 & 30 \leqslant t \leqslant 40 \\ 0 & \text{otherwise} \end{cases}$$

The graph of this function is illustrated.

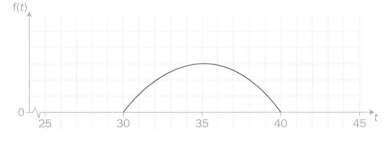

a Calculate the probability that a student took longer than 36 minutes to finish the test.

b Calculate the probability that a student took less than 32 minutes to finish the test.

c State the mean time.

d Calculate the probability that a student took longer than 36 minutes to finish the test, given that they took longer than 32 minutes.

S2

3 Exit ⟹

Summary

Refer to

- Continuous random variables are needed to describe situations involving length, time, mass, density, volume etc.
  3.1
- A probability density function has to satisfy the following conditions:
  - $f(x) \geqslant 0$ for all x and $\displaystyle\int_{-\infty}^{\infty} f(x)\,dx = 1$

  Probabilities are defined by:
  - $P(a < X < b) = \displaystyle\int_{a}^{b} f(x)\,dx$
  3.2
- The cumulative distribution function $F(x) = P(X \leqslant x)$
  3.3
- The mean and variance of a continuous random variable are found by
  - $\mu = E(X) = \displaystyle\int_{-\infty}^{\infty} x f(x)\,dx$
  - $Var(X) = \sigma^2 = E[\{X - E(X)\}^2]$
    The computational form is $\sigma^2 = E(X^2) - \mu^2$
    For a continuous random variable $E(X^2) = \displaystyle\int_{-\infty}^{\infty} x^2 f(x)\,dx$
  3.4
- The mode of a continuous random variable occurs where $f(x)$ takes its maximum value in the range over which $f(x)$ is defined. This may be at a turning point of $f(x)$, or it may be at one of the ends of the interval.
  3.5
- For a continuous random variable with cumulative distribution $F(x)$, then if m is the median, $F(m) = 0.5$
  Q_1 is the lower quartile, $F(Q_1) = 0.25$
  Q_3 is the upper quartile, $F(Q_3) = 0.75$
  3.5

Links

Any random variable which is a measurement of time, length, etc will be a continuous random variable.

Risk management is very important in the modern world. Experts can use continuous random variables to model the behaviour of natural occurrences such as floods. Insurance companies and governments can then use this information to determine whether residential developments should be allowed in specified locations.

1 If you toss a fair die 10 times, what is the probability that you will get more than one six?

2 A quality control agent tests sets of 20 components from a production line which is known to produce 95% defect-free components.

a Find the probability that a set chosen at random is free from defects.

b If he tests seven sets before lunch, find the probability that at least six of these sets were free from defects.

c He tests 120 sets in a week's work. On average, how many sets does he find which are not perfect?

3 The table shows, for a particular large company, the proportions of employees with different levels of education.

Highest education level	Degree	A-levels	5+ A*-C grades at GCSE	< 5 A*-C grades at GCSE
Proportion	0.4	0.3	0.27	0.03

A random sample of 40 people is selected.

a Determine the probability that the sample contains
  i at most 10 people with a degree
  ii exactly 2 people with less than 5 A*-C grades at GCSE
  iii more than 10 but fewer than 20 people with A levels but not a degree.

b A random sample of 750 employees is selected from the company. Find the values for the mean and variance of the number of people in the sample with degrees.

4 A supervisor expects the number of defects in a sample of a given size to follow a binomial distribution with $p = 0.05$.

a In samples of size 6, what would be the mean and variance of the number of defects if it is a binomial distribution?

The supervisor records the number of defects in 82 samples of size 6. The results are summarised in the table:

Number of defects	0	1	2	3	4	5	6
Frequency	71	8	1	0	1	1	0

b Calculate the mean and variance of the number of defects in samples of size 6.

c Do you think the binomial distribution is a good model for the number of defects in samples of a fixed size?

S2

5 Dandelions occur in a lawn at random at a rate of 0.4 per m^2.

   a Write down a suitable distribution to model the random variable X, the number of dandelions in 1 m^2 of lawn.

   b Find $P(X > 2)$.

   c Find the probability that a lawn of area 20 m^2 will contain exactly 9 dandelions.   [(c) Edexcel Limited 2000]

6 A shop sells a particular make of radio at a rate of 4 per week on average. The number sold in a week is thought to have a Poisson distribution.

   a Using a Poisson distribution, find the probability that the shop sells at least 2 in a week.

   b Find the smallest number that can be in stock at the beginning of a week in order to have at least a 99% chance of being able to meet all demands during that week.

   c Comment on the applicability of a Poisson distribution.   [(c) Edexcel Limited 2000]

7 The number of people entering a hypermarket may be modelled by a Poisson distribution with a mean rate of 4.5 people per minute.

   a Find the probability that, during a particular minute
     i   5 or fewer people enter the hypermarket
     ii exactly 5 people enter the hypermarket.

   b Find the probability that, during a two-minute interval, more than 10 people enter the supermarket.

   c When they have finished shopping, customers join a queue at one of five checkouts. State, giving a reason, whether it is likely that the number of people joining the queue at a particular checkout in any given time period may be modelled by a Poisson distribution.

8 Calls arrive at the telephone exchange of a solicitor's office randomly throughout the working day, and the number arriving in a 10-minute period has a Poisson distribution with mean 2.25.

   a Calculate the probability that the number of calls arriving between 10.30 a.m. and 10.40 a.m. is less than or equal to 1.

   b Calculate the probability that the number of calls arriving between 10.20 a.m. and 11.00 a.m. is less than or equal to 8.

   c What is the most likely number of calls in any 20-minute period?

9 In the first year of the life of a new fax machine, the number of times a maintenance engineer is required may be described by a Poisson distribution with mean 3.

a Find the probability that more than two visits by an engineer are necessary during the first year.

b If the first visit is free of charge and subsequent visits cost £40 each, determine the mean cost of maintenance in the first year.

10 A network server is left switched on and working all the time. It occasionally crashes, at an average rate of twice a week.

a Which distribution is appropriate to model the variable 'number of crashes'? Give a reason for your answer.

b Using this distribution, calculate the probability that
   i there is one crash on a Monday
   ii there are fewer than four crashes in a two-week period.

11 a State two assumptions which must be made in order to model a discrete random variable using a Poisson distribution.

Fibre optic cable produced by a particular process is known to have an average of 1.1 faults per 100 m length.

b Using an appropriate Poisson distribution, calculate the probability that there will be three or more faults in a 200 m length of cable.

The cost of repairing the faults in a length of cable is a random variable £C. C is given by the formula $C = 8X + 17$, where X is the number of faults to be repaired.

c Calculate the expected cost and the variance of the cost of repairing the faults in a 200 m length of cable.

12 a The organiser of a fund-raising event at a sports club finds that the probability that a person refuses, when asked, to buy a raffle ticket is 0.35. What is the probability that if 40 people are asked to buy a raffle ticket

   i 10 or fewer will refuse   ii exactly 15 will refuse?

   The club owns a fruit machine for the use of members. Inserting a 50p coin enables a member to attempt to win a prize. The probability of winning a prize is a constant 0.003 for each attempt made.

b Find, approximately, the probability of a member who makes 200 attempts winning 3 or more prizes.

Another member of the club asks people to pay £1 to enter a game of chance. He continues to ask people until 40 have agreed to participate.

c X is the number of people he asks before obtaining 40 participants. Say, giving a reason, whether it is likely that X will follow a binomial distribution.

13 a State two conditions under which a random variable can be modelled by a binomial distribution.

In the production of a certain electronic component it is found that 10% are defective. The component is produced in batches of 20.

b Write down a suitable model for the distribution of defective components in a batch.

c Find the probability that a batch contains

    i no defective components   **ii** more than 6 defective components.

d Find the mean and the variance of the defective components in a batch.

A supplier buys 100 components. The supplier will receive a refund if there are more than 15 defective components.

e Using a suitable approximation, find the probability that the supplier will receive a refund.

        [(c) Edexcel Limited 2004]

14 In a manufacturing process, 2% of the articles produced are defective. A batch of 200 articles is selected.

a Giving a justification for your choice, use a suitable approximation to estimate the probability that there are exactly 5 defective articles.

b Estimate the probability that there are fewer than 5 defective articles.

        [(c) Edexcel Limited 2005]

15 The continuous random variable X has cdf given by

$$F(x) = \begin{cases} 0 & x < 1 \\ (x-1)^3 & 1 \leqslant x \leqslant 2 \\ 1 & x > 2 \end{cases}$$

Find

a $P(X < 1.8)$ **b** $P(X > 0.7)$ **c** $P(1.3 < X < 1.5)$

d the median of X **e** the pdf of X.

16 The probability density function of a random variable X is given by

$$f(x) = \frac{x}{3} \quad 2 \leqslant x \leqslant k \qquad f(x) = 0 \text{ otherwise}$$

a Show that $k = \sqrt{10}$.

b Find
    i the cumulative distribution function of X
    ii $P(X < 3)$
    iii the mean and variance of X.

S2

17 Telephone calls arriving at a company switchboard are referred immediately, by the receptionist, to other people in the company. The duration of a call, in minutes, is modelled by a continuous random variable T, having probability density function

$$f(t) = \begin{cases} kt & 0 \leqslant t \leqslant 10 \\ 0 & \text{otherwise} \end{cases}$$

a Find
   i   the value of k
   ii the cumulative distribution function of T
   iii the probability that the duration of a telephone call is between 7 and 9 minutes.

b Sketch the form of the probability density function.

   A time management specialist is reviewing company records and notices that the actual duration of telephone calls is not like the model described.

c Sketch the shape of a probability density function which you feel is more realistic.

18 The continuous random variable X has probability density function

$$f(x) = \begin{cases} kx^2 & \text{for } 0 \leqslant x \leqslant 4 \\ 0 & \text{otherwise} \end{cases}$$

a Find
   i   the value of k ii the mean and variance of X.

b Calculate
   i $P(X > \mu)$ ii $P(|X - \mu| > \sigma)$
   where μ is the mean and σ is the standard deviation of X.

19 The continuous random variable X has probability density function

$$f(x) = \begin{cases} 0 & \text{for } x < 0 \\ \dfrac{1}{9}x & \text{for } 0 \leqslant x \leqslant 3 \\ \dfrac{1}{9}(6 - x) & \text{for } 3 \leqslant x \leqslant 6 \\ 0 & \text{for } x > 6 \end{cases}$$

a Sketch the probability density function.

b Explain why the mean of X is 3 without doing any calculations.

c Find the variance of X.

20 Two friends make regular telephone calls to each other. The duration, in minutes, of their telephone conversations is modelled initially by the random variable T, having probability density function

$$f(t) = \begin{cases} \frac{1}{150}(25 - t) & 5 \leqslant t \leqslant 15 \\ 0 & \text{otherwise} \end{cases}$$

a Sketch the probability density function of T.

b For all values of t, find the cumulative distribution function of T.

c Find the probability that a telephone conversation lasts longer than 12 minutes.

d Show that the median duration of a telephone conversation is given by $\left(25 - 5\sqrt{10}\right)$ minutes.

e Give a reason why this initial model may not be realistic for the distribution of durations of telephone conversations.

f Sketch the probability density function of a more realistic model. [(c) Edexcel Limited 1998]

21 The continuous random variable X has cdf given by

$$F(x) = \begin{cases} 0 & x < 0 \\ \frac{1}{64}x^3 & 0 \leqslant x \leqslant 4 \\ 1 & x > 4 \end{cases}$$

a Find   i $F(1)$ ii $F(3)$

b Show that the median of X is $2 \times \sqrt[3]{4}$

c Find the upper quartile of X.

22 The continuous random variable X has probability density function given by

$$f(x) = \begin{cases} kx(8 - x) & \text{for } 0 \leqslant x \leqslant 5 \\ 0 & \text{otherwise} \end{cases}$$

a Find the value of k.

b Sketch the probability density function.

c Find the mode of X.

23 The continuous random variable X has probability density function

$$f(x) = kx^2 \quad \text{for } 0 \leqslant x \leqslant 3, \quad f(x) = 0 \text{ otherwise}$$

a Find the value of k.

b Sketch the probability density function.

c Find the mode of X

d Find the mean and variance of X.

e Calculate $P(X > \mu + \sigma)$ where μ is the mean and σ is the standard deviation of X.

4

Sampling

This chapter will show you how to
- work with a population, a census and a sample
- consider the advantages and disadvantages of sampling
- construct the sampling distribution of a statistic.

Before you start

You should know how to:

1 List the possible outcomes in a simple experiment.

2 Find the mean and variance of simple probability distributions.

Check in:

1 James has a set of four cards with the numbers 1, 2, 3 and 4 on them. List the possible outcomes if he chooses two cards at random

   a without replacing the first card

   b replacing the first before drawing the second card.

2 The random variable X has the probability distribution

x	2	3	4
$P(X = x)$	0.3	0.3	0.4

Calculate the mean and variance.

A **sample** looks at some of a **population**.
A **census** examines the full population.

A **sampling frame** is a list of all the **units** or **elements** of the population to be sampled.
Sometimes the sampling frame does not match the population exactly.

E.g. A voting register may include people who have died and may omit people whose application forms are still being processed. In 2007 it was found that some TV companies were not including all the entrants who phoned into competition lines when drawing the competition winners.

The sample needs to be constructed so that **bias** is avoided, and ideally so that the sample will return an estimate very close to the true population **parameter** it is estimating.

Random sampling

Each member of the population has an equal chance of being selected, and *all possible combinations are equally likely.*

Simple random sampling means sampling without replacement. In practice this is usually done by using random numbers or some other random process, e.g. taking names out of a hat – if it can be done in a genuinely random way.

You do not have to deal with different types of sampling methods in this unit.

Methods of collection

Data can be collected automatically by electronic measurement devices, e.g. in a hospital or a production process; or manually through surveys, questionnaires, or direct recording.

When designing questionnaires, ensure that questions are unambiguous, simple to answer and do not bias the respondent's answer. Ensure that the data are collected in a form which is easy to analyse.

EXAMPLE 1

A population consists of all the students at an 11–18 school. Suggest at least two different sampling frames that could be used for this population.

Any system which lists all students in the school exactly once will be a sampling frame:

o Alphabetical list of all students in the school, or lists by year group or tutor group
o List of students by date of birth, with alphabetical ordering for any students with the same date of birth.

Lists of students taking boys and girls separately in any of these suggestions would produce a different sampling frame.

S2

EXAMPLE 2

Suggest possible populations and sampling frames to investigate the following:
a whether a university has a gender bias in its intake procedures
b where people in a town do their grocery shopping.

a The population is anyone who applied to the university – for one or more years depending on how extensive the investigation will be. The corresponding sampling frame will be a list of these people (any list will do).

b This example highlights some of the practical problems faced in sampling. The population of interest is the people in the town who shop for groceries, but this is not very precisely defined – and there is no easily accessible way to produce a sampling frame which lists these people.

A register for council tax collection might give the 'best available' sampling frame. Any results obtained from surveys like this need to be treated with caution.

EXAMPLE 3

The population is the people in London who voted Labour in the last general election. Explain why it is not possible to construct a sampling frame for this population.

In the UK, voting is by secret ballot, so there is no record of how people voted (though the *number* of people who voted Labour will be a matter of public record).

Exercise 4.1

1 You want to collect data on age, ethnicity, education level and gender for adults in the UK.

   a Describe the population and a possible sampling frame.

   b Explain why the sampling frame is unlikely to exactly match the population.

2 Describe the characteristics of a simple random sample.

3 A bank hires a market research company to conduct a survey of its customers to see how it could improve its service.

   a State what the population is in this situation.

   b Suggest a possible way to construct a sampling frame.

   c List any difficulties you can identify in making sure that any individual customer does not appear more than once in the sampling frame.

4 Opinions about gender roles in the household are the subject of a survey. The population is the adults living in Manchester. The sample is constructed by choosing properties in Manchester at random, consulting the council tax register and taking the first named person on the register at that address.

   Explain why this will give a biased sample.

In some circumstances taking a census is simply not possible or desirable.

Sampling is generally much cheaper than taking a census, and is almost always cost effective provided good sampling procedures are followed. A high proportion of the information available from a census can often be obtained from a sample.
In certain situations, testing items results in them being destroyed so a census is not appropriate.

However, a sample will always give *incomplete information*, while a census tells you everything about the population.

Good sampling ensures the best possible quality of information for the resources available, and avoids sources of bias. There is natural variation between individual sampling units, which is due to chance. There are also often systematic differences between groups of sampling units with one or more shared characteristics.
E.g. There are often differences between males and females.

Bias occurs where there is tendency for a sample to over- or under-represent certain groups – this is a property of the sampling *method* rather than the sample itself.
e.g. If a sample of 50 people is taken by simple random sampling using a council tax register which has equal numbers of males and females on it then, even if the sample ends up with 22 men and 28 women, there is no bias present. However, if the method used is to select a property at random and to take the first named person on the register at that property, then the sample will be biased because the first named person will more often be male.

There are a number of common sources of bias:

- Subjective choice by person taking the sample
  E.g. A person conducting a survey in a town centre may ask only people who 'look respectable' because they are thought more likely to agree to participate.

- Self-selection
  E.g. Radio phone-in surveys are strongly biased. Only people who feel particularly strongly on the issue will participate.

○ **Non-response**
E.g. Almost all surveys have an element of 'self-selection' in them because some people surveyed may choose not to take part. Companies conducting surveys will often offer inducements – entry into a prize draw for example – to encourage people to take part.

○ **Convenience sampling (opportunity sampling)**
E.g. Items are chosen by the easiest method of sampling rather than in any structured and systematic attempt to construct an unbiased sample.

○ **Sampling from an incomplete sampling frame**
E.g. If you use a telephone directory or a list of registered voters as a sampling frame for the population of adults in a community then there will be groups of people who are seriously under-represented.

Exercise 4.2

1 An airline sends out a postal questionnaire to enquire about customers views on a new route they are introducing. They say that all completed questionnaires will be entered into a draw to win free flights on this new route.

   a Explain why the sample is biased.

   b Explain why the airline might make this offer.

2 Give an example of a convenience sample.

3 A manufacturer of mobile phone batteries wants to know how long they will operate before needing to be charged.

   a Explain why a sample should be used rather than a census.

   The batteries are packed in boxes of 50 as they come off the production line. A manager suggests taking one of the boxes and sending them to be tested as the sample.

   b Assuming 50 is a reasonable size of sample to take, do you think this is a good way to choose the batteries to be tested? Give any advantages and disadvantages you can see with the method and suggest an alternative if you do not think this is a good way to do it.

4 A bank hires a market research company to conduct a survey of its customers to see how it could improve its service.

   a Explain why a sample is more appropriate here than a census.

   b Can you think of any reasons why the bank might not want just to take a simple random sample of its customers?

In this section, when analysing results of sampling, you can assume that a simple random sampling method has been used, i.e. all possible combinations of sampling units are equally likely to be chosen, and the method is unbiased.

See **S1** for revision.

EXAMPLE 1

A pair of dice is thrown repeatedly and the average score on the two dice is taken. What is the probability distribution for this?

The probability distribution of X is:

X	1	1.5	2	2.5	3	3.5	4	4.5	5	5.5	6
$P(X = x)$	$\frac{1}{36}$	$\frac{2}{36}$	$\frac{3}{36}$	$\frac{4}{36}$	$\frac{5}{36}$	$\frac{6}{36}$	$\frac{5}{36}$	$\frac{4}{36}$	$\frac{3}{36}$	$\frac{2}{36}$	$\frac{1}{36}$

If you throw a fair die n times and take the average of the scores, you have taken a simple random sample. For any value of n (in theory) you could work out a probability distribution.

The mean of the n throws is called a statistic (it depends only on the values observed in the random sample). The probability distribution is known as the sampling distribution of the statistic.

Examples of other statistics are the median, the standard deviation, the range, etc., and the sampling distributions for some of these can be surprisingly complicated. Fortunately the ones which are most useful have relatively simple distributions, or can be approximated by something simple.

EXAMPLE 2

The heights of 15-year-old males in a large town have a mean μ and a standard deviation σ. The heights of a sample of twenty 15-year-old males were recorded as $x_1, x_2, x_3, \ldots, x_{20}$. Which of the following are statistics? For any which are not, explain why they are not.

a $\displaystyle\sum_{i=1}^{20} x_i$

b $\displaystyle\sum_{i=1}^{20} (x_i - \mu)^2$

c $\displaystyle\sum_{i=1}^{20} (x_i - \bar{x})^2$ where $\bar{x} = \dfrac{1}{20}\displaystyle\sum_{i=1}^{20} x_i$

d The largest of the values $x_1, x_2, x_3, \ldots, x_{20}$

S2

EXAMPLE 2 (CONT.)

e The range of the sample values

f $\dfrac{x_1 - \mu}{\sigma}$

g The number of values $x_1, x_2, x_3, \ldots, x_{20}$ which are greater than μ

h The number of values $x_1, x_2, x_3, \ldots, x_{20}$ which are greater than $\bar{x}$

A statistic must depend on some or all of the values of sample observations, and not on anything else, so **a, c, d, e** and **h** are all statistics.

b and **g** need the value of μ, and **f** needs the values of μ and σ, so these three are not statistics.

μ and $\bar{x}$ represent the population mean and sample mean respectively.

One of the simplest situations is when the 'measurement' of each member of a sample can be modelled by a random variable taking the value 1 when some criterion is satisfied and 0 when it is not.

E.g. If a light bulb on a production line is faulty.

In this case, the sampling distribution of a sample of size n will be a binomial random variable with parameters n and p where p is the probability that the criterion is satisfied for any individual.

EXAMPLE 3

20% of the trainee teachers in a college are male. A random sample of 15 teachers is taken from the college. The random variables X_i: $i = 1, 2, 3, \ldots, 15$ are defined as

$$X_i = \begin{cases} 1 & \text{if the } i\text{th trainee teacher is male} \\ 0 & \text{if the } i\text{th trainee teacher is female} \end{cases}$$

a Write down the distribution for $\displaystyle\sum_{i=1}^{15} X_i$

b Find $\mathrm{P}\left(\displaystyle\sum_{i=1}^{15} X_i = 3\right)$.

c Give the values of $\mathrm{E}\left(\displaystyle\sum_{i=1}^{15} X_i\right)$ and $\mathrm{Var}\left(\displaystyle\sum_{i=1}^{15} X_i\right)$.

a This is a binomial distribution with $n = 15$ and $p = 0.2$.

b 0.231 (from tables or by the formula)

c $\mathrm{E}\left(\displaystyle\sum_{i=1}^{15} X_i\right) = np = 15 \times 0.2 = 3$

$\mathrm{Var}\left(\displaystyle\sum_{i=1}^{15} X_i\right) = npq = 15 \times 0.2 \times 0.8 = 2.4$

89

In other situations, you may be able to derive a sampling distribution directly from listing possible outcomes and their associated probabilities.

3/6   2/6   1/6

A bag contains three 50p coins, two £1 coins and a £2 coin. Two coins are taken from the bag. Find the sampling distribution of the mean value of the coins taken.

Construct a table showing the 30 (equally likely) possible outcomes of taking two coins from this bag and their mean value:

X	0.5	0.5	0.5	1	1	2
0.5		0.5	0.5	0.75	0.75	1.25
0.5	0.5		0.5	0.75	0.75	1.25
0.5	0.5	0.5		0.75	0.75	1.25
1	0.75	0.75	0.75		1	1.5
1	0.75	0.75	0.75	1		1.5
2	1.25	1.25	1.25	1.5	1.5	

Produce a table for the sampling distribution:

x	0.5	0.75	1	1.25	1.5
P(X = x)	$\frac{6}{30}$	$\frac{12}{30}$	$\frac{2}{30}$	$\frac{6}{30}$	$\frac{4}{30}$

From this very simple situation, you get quite a strange looking distribution.

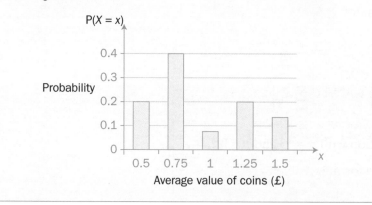

EXAMPLE 5

How would the sampling distribution of Example 4 be different if you had a really large bag of coins with the 50p, £1 and £2 coins in the ratio of 3:2:1?

You could model this by thinking of using the same bag as in Example 4, but replace each coin after noting its value.

The table and probability distribution then look like this:

Y	0.5	0.5	0.5	1	1	2
0.5	0.5	0.5	0.5	0.75	0.75	1.25
0.5	0.5	0.5	0.5	0.75	0.75	1.25
0.5	0.5	0.5	0.5	0.75	0.75	1.25
1	0.75	0.75	0.75	1	1	1.5
1	0.75	0.75	0.75	1	1	1.5
2	1.25	1.25	1.25	1.5	1.5	2

The change in likelihood is very small when there is a large number of each type of coin.

y	0.5	0.75	1	1.25	1.5	2
$P(Y=y)$	$\dfrac{9}{36}$	$\dfrac{12}{36}$	$\dfrac{4}{36}$	$\dfrac{6}{36}$	$\dfrac{4}{36}$	$\dfrac{1}{36}$

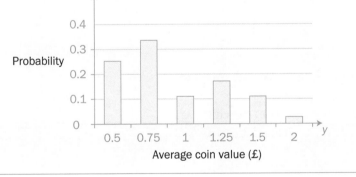

Exercise 4.3

1 The incomes of doctors working for a large health trust have a mean μ and a standard deviation σ. The incomes of a sample of twenty doctors working for the trust are recorded as $x_1, x_2, x_3, \ldots, x_{20}$.

Which of these are statistics? For any which are not, explain why they are not.

a $x_1 - x_2$

b $\sum\limits_{i=1}^{20}(x_i - 80000)^2$

c $\sum\limits_{i=1}^{20}(x_i - \bar{x})^2$ where $\bar{x} = \dfrac{1}{20}\sum\limits_{i=1}^{20}x_i$

d The median of the values $x_1, x_2, x_3, \ldots, x_{20}$

e $\dfrac{\bar{x} - \mu}{\sigma}$

2 One third of the members of a large fitness club are over 40 years old. A random sample of 20 members is taken from the club. The random variables X_i: $i = 1, 2, 3, \ldots, 20$ are defined as

$$X_i = \begin{cases} 1 & \text{if the } i\text{th member is over 40} \\ 0 & \text{if the } i\text{th member is not over 40} \end{cases}$$

a Write down the distribution for $\sum\limits_{i=1}^{20}X_i$

b Find $P\left(\sum\limits_{i=1}^{20}X_i = 2\right)$

c Give the values of $E\left(\sum\limits_{i=1}^{20}X_i\right)$ and $\text{Var}\left(\sum\limits_{i=1}^{20}X_i\right)$

3 Three quarters of the members of a large cycle club own more than one bike. A random sample of 10 members is taken from the club. The random variables X_i: $i = 1, 2, 3, \ldots, 10$ are defined as

$$X_i = \begin{cases} 1 & \text{if the } i\text{th member owns more than one bike} \\ 0 & \text{if the } i\text{th member does not own more than one bike} \end{cases}$$

a Write down the distribution for $\sum\limits_{i=1}^{10}X_i$

b Find $P\left(\sum\limits_{i=1}^{10}X_i \leqslant 7\right)$

c Give the values of $E\left(\sum\limits_{i=1}^{10}X_i\right)$ and $\text{Var}\left(\sum\limits_{i=1}^{10}X_i\right)$

4   A video game machine takes tokens for one game and for three games. 20% of the tokens used are for one game.

   a   Find the mean μ for the number of games per token.

   A random sample of three tokens is taken when the machine is emptied.

   b   List all possible samples.

   c   Find the sampling distribution for the mean number of games per token.

   d   Find the sampling distribution for the mode of the number of games per token.

   e   Find the sampling distribution for the median of the number of games per token.

5   Another video game machine takes tokens for one game, for three games and for six games. The number of tokens used are in the ratio $1:2:2$ for 1, 3 and 6 games.

   a   Find the mean μ for the number of games per token.

   A random sample of two tokens is taken when the machine is emptied.

   b   List all possible samples and the probability that each of these possible samples is taken.

   c   Find the sampling distribution for the mean number of games per token.

   d   Find the sampling distribution for the median of the number of games per token.

S2

1   The Principal of a school wants some information on the number of pupils who were absent each day in the school year 2007–08.

He records the number who were absent on each of 30 Mondays.

   a   Why is this sampling procedure likely to be biased?

   b   Suggest a better procedure he could use.   [(c) Edexcel Limited 1996]

2   a   Explain briefly what you understand by

       i   a population   ii   a sampling frame.

   b   A market research organisation wants to take a sample of
       i   owners of diesel motor cars in the UK
       ii   persons living in Oxford who suffered from injuries to the back during July 1996.
   Suggest a suitable sampling frame in each case.   [(c) Edexcel Limited 1997]

3   A librarian wishes to establish the number of times books in the library are borrowed during the course of a year.

   a   Suggest a suitable sampling frame.

   b   Identify the sampling units.

   c   Explain *briefly* how the librarian could take a sample for this purpose.

A sixth former examined the books returned by 100 people using the library one Saturday. She calculated that the mean number of times these books had been borrowed over the last 12 months was 8.2. The librarian said that the mean value for all the books in the library is unlikely to be close to 8.2.

   d   State, giving a reason, whether you would expect the mean value for all the books to be higher or lower than 8.2.   [(c) Edexcel Limited 1995]

4   The committee of a squash club are discussing whether or not to incorporate a sauna as part of the club's facilities.
It is decided to ask a sample of members for their views.

   a   Suggest a suitable sampling frame.

   b   Explain the difference between a sample and a census, using this example to illustrate your answer.

   c   State why you think the committee might have decided to take a sample in this case rather than a census.   [(c) Edexcel Limited 1996]

S2

5 A library wishes to investigate whether there is a problem with damage to its books so a sample of the books is to be checked.

    a   Give one advantage and one disadvantage of taking a sample as opposed to a census.

    b   Suggest a possible sampling frame.

    c   Describe the sampling units.

The librarian was told to take the top two shelves of children's books as the sample.

    d   State, giving a reason, whether or not you feel this would be a sensible procedure.

6 In each of the following cases, give **two** reasons to explain why the sampling procedure is **not** satisfactory.

    a   The population is housewives living in the Greater Manchester area. To get a random sample, an interviewer questions women he meets near the Arndale shopping Centre on a Monday morning after 9 a.m.

    b   The population is all animal feed suppliers in Northumberland. A researcher first lists all those in the Yellow Pages. This gives a list of 36 firms. They are assigned a number from 1 to 36. Then an ordinary die is rolled six times and the total determines which firm is chosen. This is repeated to get the random sample.

    c   The population is all voters in Wales. To get a random sample a researcher takes the telephone directory for Wales, drops the book until it falls open at a page, then with his eyes closed sticks a pin in it. The number closest to the pin is the one rung. This is repeated to get a sample of voters.

7 a   Explain what you understand by

        i   a population
        ii a sampling frame.

The population and the sampling frame may not be the same.

    b   Explain why this might be the case.

    c   Give an example, justifying your choices, to illustrate when you might use

        i   a census
        ii a sample.

S2

4

Exit →

Summary   Refer to

⊙ You can use a sample to gather information about a population when a
census would be impractical. You need to construct the sample carefully
to avoid bias.   4.1–4.2

⊙ A sampling frame is a list of all the sampling units or elements (often people)
in the population to be sampled.   4.1

⊙ A statistic is a function that depends only on the observed values in a sample
i.e. it must not use any parameter values.
The probability distribution is known as the sampling distribution of the statistic.   4.3

Links

Collecting data and testing products can be costly and
time consuming. Sampling methods allow the relevant
information to be gathered more efficiently. Research
into the development of the related techniques is ongoing.

In industry, quality control techniques rely on sampling
methods. It would be very costly for a company to test
every product made on a production line, so instead they
check a sample of their products and use the results to
determine if their quality standards are met overall.

S2

5

Continuous distributions

This chapter will show you how to
- calculate probabilities and the mean, variance and standard deviation of a uniform continuous random variable
- approximate the binomial distribution by a normal distribution
- approximate the Poisson distribution by a normal distribution.

Before you start

You should know how to:

1 Find the mean and variance of a binomial distribution.

2 Find the mean and variance of a Poisson distribution.

3 Calculate probabilities using the normal distribution.

Check in:

1 If $X \sim B(8, 0.3)$, find the mean and variance of X.

2 If $X \sim Po(7.3)$, find the mean and variance of X.

3 $X \sim N(4, 9)$. Find

   a $P(X < 10)$

   b $P(X > 5)$

   c $P(|X| < 3)$

S2

Any continuous variable will usually be measured correct to a particular degree of accuracy.

e.g. A sprinter's time for 100 metres may be recorded as 10.32 seconds, but this means that his actual time was somewhere between 10.315 and 10.325 seconds.

As a first approximation model the distribution of the rounding error, E, as being uniform over the range from −0.005 to +0.005.

Since the total probability is the area under the pdf, it follows that the pdf must be

$$f(e) = \begin{cases} 100 & -0.005 \leqslant e \leqslant 0.005 \\ 0 & \text{otherwise} \end{cases}$$

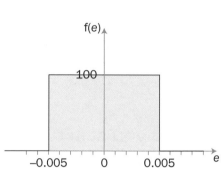

This type of distribution is known as a **uniform continuous distribution** or a **rectangular distribution**.

The properties of a uniform distribution are:

○ it takes the same value over the range in which it is defined
○ it has no mode
○ it is symmetric about its mid-range value. Therefore the mean and median will both be equal to the mid-range of the distribution.

The mean and median are both 0 in the sprinter example.

If a **continuous random variable**, X, has a uniform distribution over the interval (α, β), then its **probability density function** will be given by

$$f(x) = \begin{cases} \dfrac{1}{\beta - \alpha} & \alpha \leqslant x \leqslant \beta \\ 0 & \text{otherwise} \end{cases}$$

$$\text{median} = \text{mean} = E(X) = \frac{\alpha + \beta}{2} \quad \text{and} \quad \text{Var}(X) = \frac{(\beta - \alpha)^2}{12}$$

The **cumulative distribution function** is given by

$$F(x) = \begin{cases} 0 & x \leqslant \alpha \\ \dfrac{x - \alpha}{\beta - \alpha} & \alpha \leqslant x \leqslant \beta \\ 1 & x \leqslant \beta \end{cases}$$

Proof of the variance result:

$$\mu = E(X) = \int_\alpha^\beta x\left(\frac{1}{\beta - \alpha}\right)dx$$

$$= \left[\left(\frac{1}{\beta - \alpha}\right)\frac{x^2}{2}\right]_\alpha^\beta$$

$$= \left(\frac{1}{\beta - \alpha}\right)\frac{(\beta^2 - \alpha^2)}{2}$$

$$= \frac{\beta + \alpha}{2}$$

$$E(X^2) = \int_\alpha^\beta x^2\left(\frac{1}{\beta - \alpha}\right)dx$$

$$= \left[\left(\frac{1}{\beta - \alpha}\right)\frac{x^3}{3}\right]_\alpha^\beta$$

$$= \left(\frac{1}{\beta - \alpha}\right)\frac{(\beta^3 - \alpha^3)}{3}$$

$$= \frac{\beta^2 + \alpha\beta + \alpha^2}{3}$$

Therefore

$$Var(X) = E(X^2) - \mu^2 = \frac{\beta^2 + \alpha\beta + \alpha^2}{3} - \left(\frac{\beta + \alpha}{2}\right)^2$$

$$= \frac{4\beta^2 + 4\alpha\beta + 4\alpha^2 - 3\beta^2 - 6\alpha\beta - 3\alpha^2}{12}$$

$$= \frac{\beta^2 - 2\alpha\beta + \alpha^2}{12} = \frac{(\beta - \alpha)^2}{12}$$

You may be asked to prove these results in the examination.

S2

The continuous random variable, X, is uniformly distributed over the interval $(5, 12)$. Find

a $E(X)$ b $Var(X)$ c $P(X < 10)$

a $E(X) = \frac{5 + 12}{2} = 8.5$

b $Var(X) = \frac{(12 - 5)^2}{12} = \frac{49}{12}$

c $P(X < 10) = \frac{5}{7}$

You could find $P(X < 10)$ by integrating the pdf. Alternatively, note that the area is $\frac{5}{7}$ of the area under the whole pdf (which is 1).

EXAMPLE 2

A road is being repaired and temporary telephones are installed at intervals of 1 km.

A motorist breaks down on the road and can see 100 metres in either direction, but cannot see a phone. He tosses a coin to decide whether to walk forwards or backwards until he finds one.

a Show that the distance he walks is uniformly distributed over the interval $(100, 900)$.

b Show that the mean distance he walks is half a kilometre.

c Find the probability that he has to walk less than a quarter of a kilometre.

---

a Since he can see 100 metres in each direction, he has to walk at least 100 m. If a phone is just out of sight in the direction he does not take then the first one he comes to will be 900 metres away.

b The mean is $\dfrac{(100 + 900)}{2} = 500 \text{ metres} = \dfrac{1}{2} \text{ km}$

c $P(\text{walks} < 250\,\text{m}) = \dfrac{250 - 100}{900 - 100} = \dfrac{150}{800} = \dfrac{3}{16}$

Exercise 5.1

1 Find $E(X)$ and $Var(X)$ for the continuous random variables with probability density functions given by

a $f(x) = \begin{cases} \dfrac{1}{8} & 0 \leqslant x \leqslant 8 \\ 0 & \text{otherwise} \end{cases}$

b $f(x) = \begin{cases} \dfrac{1}{3} & 12 \leqslant x \leqslant 15 \\ 0 & \text{otherwise} \end{cases}$

c $f(x) = \begin{cases} \dfrac{1}{10} & -5 \leqslant x \leqslant 5 \\ 0 & \text{otherwise} \end{cases}$

2 Find $E(X)$ and $Var(X)$ for the uniform continuous random variables defined on the intervals

a $(0, 4)$ **b** $(5, 9)$

c $(-8, -4)$ **d** $(-2, 8)$

3 The continuous random variable X has the probability density function shown in the diagram. From first principles, find

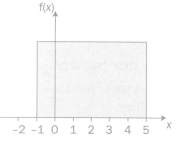

  a $E(X)$

  b $Var(X)$

  c $P(X < 0)$.

4 X is a uniform continuous random variable with $E(X) = 7$ and $Var(X) = \frac{1}{3}$. Find

  a the probability density function of X

  b the cumulative distribution function $F(x)$.

5 X is a uniform continuous random variable with $E(X) = -3$ and $Var(X) = 5$.
  Find $P(X < 0)$.

6 Lengths of steel pins are measured correct to the nearest 0.1 cm. X is the continuous random variable which represents the measurement error for one of the pins.

  a Give the probability density function for X.

  b Find $Var(X)$.

  c Find the lower quartile of X.

7 An assistant in a curtain shop throws away the end of a roll of material if its length is less than 60 cm. Assuming that these lengths may be modelled by a uniform distribution, find the mean and variance of the lengths thrown away from a roll of material.

8 In a fairground game, lines are drawn across a flat board at 4 cm intervals. Players roll their own coin down a track onto the board. When the coin stops, if it touches one of the lines then the player loses his coin, but if the coin lies completely between the two lines the player has his own coin returned and wins another of the same value.

  a A 10p coin has a diameter of 24.5 mm. Find the probability that a player using a 10p coin will lose it.

  b A £1 coin has a diameter of 22.5 mm. Without doing detailed calculations, explain why a player is less likely to lose a £1 coin than a 10p coin.

  c The smallest coin in normal use in the UK is the 5p with a diameter of 18 mm. The fairground operator will not allow people to use a 5p piece to play the game – can you explain why?

S2

Continuity correction

Discrete random variables take only particular values, each with its own probability.

Continuous random variables take values over an interval, and probabilities are defined for ranges of values rather than individual values.

When there is a large number of possible values for a discrete distribution the shape of the graph of the distribution can look similar to the normal distribution.

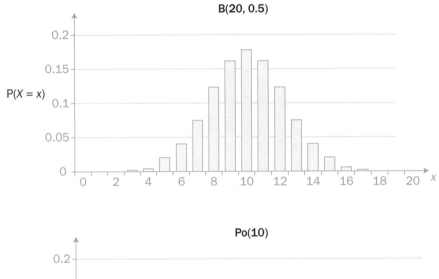

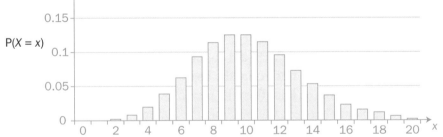

The discrete probabilities are shown as bars with gaps between them. The bars really should have zero width since the probability occurs only at the integer value, in which case the diagrams would not look so much like the normal distribution.

[If you represent each value x_0 in the discrete distribution by the interval $(x_0 - 0.5, x_0 + 0.5)$], which are the values that round to x_0, then the graphs look like these:

E.g. The value 7 will be represented by the interval $(6.5, 7.5)$, i.e $6.5 \leqslant X < 7.5$.

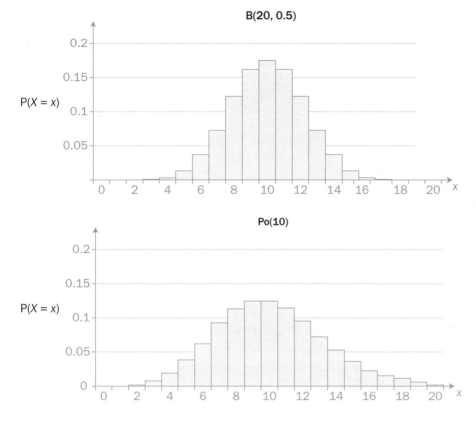

Both of these distributions have a mean of 10. However the standard deviation of the binomial is less than that of the Poisson.

The resemblance to the normal distribution is now even stronger. When you use the normal distribution to approximate the binomial (and the Poisson) you must use a continuity correction.

E.g. If you want $P(X > 7)$ you must use a cut-off for the normal at 7.5.
For $P(X < 7)$ or $P(X \geqslant 7)$ the cut-off would be at 6.5.

The easiest way to determine whether the cut-off is at +0.5 or at −0.5 is to consider which two integers are to be separated.

Hence,

$$P(X = x) \approx P(x - 0.5 < Y < x + 0.5)$$

where Y is the approximating normal random variable.

Because the distribution is continuous it doesn't matter whether you use < or ⩽ on either of these limits.

EXAMPLE 1

Let $X \sim \mathrm{B}(n, p)$ and $Y \sim \mathrm{N}(np, np(1 - p))$ where n, p satisfy the conditions needed for Y to be used as an approximation for X. Write down the probability you need to calculate for Y (including the continuity correction) as the approximation for each of these probabilities for X.

a $\mathrm{P}(X < 15)$

b $\mathrm{P}(X > 12)$

c $\mathrm{P}(X \leqslant 17)$

d $\mathrm{P}(12 < X \leqslant 15)$

---

a $\mathrm{P}(Y < 14.5)$

b $\mathrm{P}(Y > 12.5)$

c $\mathrm{P}(Y \leqslant 17.5)$

d $\mathrm{P}(12.5 \leqslant Y \leqslant 15.5)$

The integers which satisfy this are 13, 14 and 15.

Since the normal distribution is continuous it requires only one calculation for each block of individual values.

The parameters for the normal approximation

If $X \sim \mathrm{B}(n, p)$ then

See Chapter 1 for revision.

$$\mathrm{E}(X) = np \quad \text{and} \quad \mathrm{Var}(X) = npq = np(1 - p)$$

If n is large and p is close to 0.5, so that the distribution is nearly symmetrical, then you can use the normal distribution to approximate the binomial.

The general rule is that the normal distribution can be used as an approximation when both np and $n(1 - p)$ are >5.

The parameters to be used are the mean and variance of the binomial:

$$\mu = np, \quad \sigma^2 = npq$$

If p is small then $1 - p$ is close to 1 and np is close to npq. In these circumstances (n large, p small enough that np is small) you can use the $\mathrm{Po}(\lambda)$ distribution as an approximation, where $\lambda = np$ is the Poisson parameter to be used.

Never approximate the binomial by a Poisson and then approximate from the Poisson to the normal – use npq as the normal variance directly from the distribution.

EXAMPLE 2

If $X \sim B(30, 0.4)$ calculate $P(8 \leqslant X \leqslant 15)$

a from the tables of binomial probabilities

b by using a normal approximation.

a $P(8 \leqslant X \leqslant 15) = P(X \leqslant 15) - P(X \leqslant 7)$
$$= 0.9029 - 0.0435 = 0.8594$$

b For the binomial, $\mu = np = 30 \times 0.4 = 12$;
$\sigma^2 = npq = 30 \times 0.4 \times 0.6 = 7.2$,
so use the $N(12, 7.2)$ distribution to approximate the $B(30, 0.4)$ distribution.

The continuity correction says
$P(8 \leqslant X \leqslant 15) \approx P(7.5 < Y < 15.5)$,
where Y is the approximating normal random variable.

$$P(7.5 < Y < 15.5) = P\left(\frac{7.5 - 12}{\sqrt{7.2}} < Z < \frac{15.5 - 12}{\sqrt{7.2}} \right)$$
$$= \Phi(1.304) - \Phi(-1.677)$$
$$= 0.9032 - (1 - 0.9532) = 0.8574$$
$$= 0.857 \text{ (3 s.f.)}$$

This calculation has been done using interpolation in reading the normal tables. You are not required to do this, but it is good statistical practice.

S2

An airline estimates that 7% of passengers who book seats on a flight do not turn up to take their seat. On one flight for which there are 185 available seats the airline sells 197 tickets. Find the probability that they will have to refuse boarding to any passengers holding a valid ticket for that flight.

The number of 'no shows', X, can be modelled by a $B(197, 0.07)$ distribution if we make the simplifying assumption that all passengers behave independently of one another (a reasonable assumption in most cases but not always).
You want $P(X < 12)$.

Use $Y \sim N(185 \times 0.07, 185 \times 0.07 \times 0.93) = N(12.95, 12.0435)$ to approximate, and calculate $P(Y < 11.5)$ using the continuity correction:

$$P(Y < 11.5) = P\left(Z < \frac{11.5 - 12.95}{\sqrt{12.0435}} \right) = \Phi(-0.418)$$
$$= 1 - 0.6621 = 0.3379 = 0.338 \text{ (3 s.f.)}$$

The airline will have to refuse boarding if there are fewer than 12 'no shows'.

Exercise 5.2

1 Let $X \sim B(n, p)$ and $Y \sim N(np, np(1-p))$ where n, p satisfy the conditions needed for Y to be used as an approximation for X. Write down the probability you need to calculate for Y (including the continuity correction) as the approximation for each of the following probabilities for X.

a $P(X < 42)$ b $P(X > 31)$

c $P(X \geqslant 9)$ d $P(42 < X \leqslant 85)$

2 Which of these distributions could reasonably be approximated by a normal distribution? For those which can, give the normal which would be used.

a $X \sim B(50, 0.7)$ b $X \sim B(10, 0.7)$

c $X \sim B(500, 0.2)$ d $X \sim B(500, 0.002)$

3 Use normal approximations to calculate

a $P(X < 42)$ if $X \sim B(50, 0.7)$

b $P(X \geqslant 9)$ if $X \sim B(40, 0.3)$

c $P(X \geqslant 13)$ if $X \sim B(34, 0.37)$

d $P(25 < X \leqslant 37)$ if $X \sim B(80, 0.4)$

e $P(43 \leqslant X \leqslant 55)$ if $X \sim B(124, 0.43)$

4 $X \sim B(50, 0.3)$

a Calculate $P(12 < X < 20)$
  i using tables
  ii using a normal approximation.

b i What error is there in using the normal approximation?
  ii Express this error as a percentage of the exact probability.

5 Explain briefly the conditions under which the normal distribution can be used as an approximation to a binomial distribution. If the conditions are satisfied, state what normal distribution would be used to approximate the $X \sim B(n, p)$ distribution.

6 On a production line, on average 6% of the bottles of lemonade are not filled properly.

   a If 5 bottles are examined, find the probability that exactly one of them is not filled properly.

   b If 25 bottles are examined, use a Poisson approximation to find the probability that not more than 3 of them are not filled properly.

   c If 2000 bottles are examined, use a normal approximation to find the probability that fewer than 100 are not filled properly.

7 A multiple choice test has 50 questions, each with 4 possible answers.

   a If Catharine guesses the answer to each question randomly, state the exact distribution of X, the number of answers Catharine gets correct.

   b If the test has a pass mark of 20, find the probability that Catharine passes the test.

   c Shopna takes the same test, but knows enough to be able to rule out one of the possible answers to each question. Use a normal approximation to find the probability that Shopna fails the test.

8 A Health Trust issues guidance to doctors that they should show any patients with raised blood pressure some information on lifestyle which would help bring down their blood pressure. The doctors in one surgery get their research assistant to look at the patient records and find that 35% of their patients have raised blood pressure.

   a The surgery has 84 patients booked for appointments on the following day. Assuming that these 84 patients are a random sample from all the patients registered with that surgery, find the probability that at least 25 will have raised blood pressure.

   b Comment on the assumption made in part **a** that the people with appointments at the surgery on the following day will be a random sample from all people on the register.

S2

thymine

5.3 | Normal approximation to the Poisson distribution

For a Poisson distribution with large λ (>10) you would often use a normal distribution as an approximation, particularly when the probability of an interval is required, e.g. $P(X \geqslant 15)$ or $P(6 < X < 14)$, since this will be a single calculation in a continuous distribution but will involve multiple calculations in a discrete distribution.

> Remember that the normal distribution uses the standard deviation to calculate the z-score, i.e. $z = \dfrac{x - \lambda}{\sqrt{\lambda}}$
>
> Remember to include the continuity correction.

The parameters used are the mean and variance of the Poisson, i.e. $\mu = \sigma^2 = \lambda$

EXAMPLE 1

If $X \sim \text{Po}(10)$, calculate $P(8 \leqslant X \leqslant 15)$

a from the tables of Poisson probabilities

b by using a normal approximation.

---

a $P(8 \leqslant X \leqslant 15) = P(X \leqslant 15) - P(X \leqslant 7)$

$\qquad\qquad\qquad = 0.9513 - 0.2202$

$\qquad\qquad\qquad = 0.7311$

b For the Poisson, $\mu = \lambda = 10$; $\sigma^2 = \lambda = 10$,
so use the $N(10, 10)$ distribution to approximate the $\text{Po}(10)$ distribution.

The continuity correction gives
$P(8 \leqslant X \leqslant 15) \approx P(7.5 < Y < 15.5)$
where Y is the approximating normal.

$P(7.5 < Y < 15.5) = P\left(\dfrac{7.5 - 10}{\sqrt{10}} < Z < \dfrac{15.5 - 10}{\sqrt{10}} \right)$

$\qquad\qquad\qquad = \Phi(1.739) - \Phi(-0.791)$

$\qquad\qquad\qquad = 0.9590 - (1 - 0.7855)$

$\qquad\qquad\qquad = 0.7455$

$\qquad\qquad\qquad = 0.746 \text{ (3 s.f.)}$

This calculation was done using interpolation in reading the normal tables. Without interpolation the end would be
$\Phi(1.74) - \Phi(-0.79)$
$\quad = 0.9591 - (1 - 0.7852)$
$\quad = 0.7433 = 0.743 \text{ (3 s.f.)}$

S2

EXAMPLE 2

The demand for a particular spare part in a car accessory shop may be modelled by a Poisson distribution. On average the demand per week for that part is 5.5.

a The shop has 7 in stock at the start of one week. What is the probability that they will not be able to supply everyone who asks for that part during the week?

b The manager, who is going to be away for four weeks, wants to leave sufficient stock so that there is no more than a 5% probability of running out of any parts while he is away. How many of this particular spare part should he have in stock when he leaves?

---

a For the demand in a week, use the Po(5.5) distribution, for which there are tables. Then if the demand is $\leqslant 7$ the shop can supply all the customers. The probability of not being able to supply all the demand is $1 - 0.8095 = 0.1905$.

b For the demand in four weeks, use the Po(22) distribution, which can be approximated by the N(22, 22) distribution.

You need to find k so that

$$P(\text{demand} \leqslant k) > 0.95$$

$\Phi^{-1}(0.95) = 1.6449$ so you need to find the smallest integer k which satisfies $\dfrac{k - 22}{\sqrt{22}} > 1.6449$, which is 30 (solution is $k > 29.7$).

Exercise 5.3

1 Let $X \sim \text{Po}(\lambda)$ and $Y \sim \text{N}(\lambda, \lambda)$, where λ satisfies the conditions needed for Y to be used as an approximation for X.
Write down the probability you need to calculate for Y (including the continuity correction) as the approximation for each of these probabilities for X.

a $P(X < 16)$

b $P(X > 22)$

c $P(X \leqslant 17)$

d $P(45 \leqslant X < 62)$

2 Which of these distributions could reasonably be approximated by a normal distribution?
For those which can, give the normal distribution that would be used.

   a $X \sim \text{Po}(16)$

   b $X \sim \text{Po}(12.32)$

   c $X \sim \text{Po}(8.5)$

3 Use normal approximations to calculate

   a $P(X < 42)$ if $X \sim \text{Po}(49)$

   b $P(X \geqslant 9)$ if $X \sim \text{Po}(12.3)$

   c $P(X \geqslant 13)$ if $X \sim \text{Po}(18.4)$

   d $P(25 < X \leqslant 37)$ if $X \sim \text{Po}(21)$

   e $P(43 \leqslant X \leqslant 55)$ if $X \sim \text{Po}(51.34)$

4 $X \sim \text{Po}(10)$

   a Calculate $P(7 < X < 14)$
      i using tables
      ii using a normal approximation.

   b i What error is there in using the normal approximation?
      ii Express this as a percentage of the exact probability.

5 Explain briefly the conditions under which the normal distribution can be used as an approximation to a Poisson distribution.
If the conditions are satisfied, state which normal distribution would be used to approximate the $X \sim \text{Po}(\lambda)$ distribution.

6 The number of accidents that occur on a particular stretch of road in a day can be modelled by a Poisson distribution with parameter 0.5.

   a Find the probability that during a week (7 days) exactly 2 accidents occur on that stretch of road.

   b Find the probability that during a month (30 days) at least 20 accidents occur on that stretch of road.

7 The number of letters delivered to a house on a day may be modelled by a Poisson distribution with parameter 1.5.

   a Find the probability that there are 2 letters delivered on a particular day.

   b The home owner is away for 3 weeks (18 days of post).
   Find the probability that there will be more than 25 letters waiting for him when he gets back.

8 The number of errors on a page of a book can be modelled by
   a Poisson distribution with parameter 0.15. The book has
   167 pages. Find the probability that there are no more than
   20 errors in the book.

9 The number of earth tremors over a certain strength which occur
   in a particular part of California in a week may be modelled by a
   Poisson distribution with parameter 2.25.

   a Find the probability that during a 4-week period exactly
      8 tremors over this strength occur in that part of California.

   b Taking a year as 52 weeks, find, approximately, the probability
      that during a year at least 100 tremors over this strength
      occur in that part of California.

   c Find the probability that during a leap year (366 days) at least
      100 tremors over this strength occur in that part of California.

10 The number of letters delivered to an office on a day (Mon–Sat)
   may be modelled by a Poisson distribution with parameter 7.5.

   a Find the probability that there are 10 letters delivered on a
      particular day.

   The office is closed for a week for refurbishment and the
   Post Office is asked to hold the mail until the
   following Monday.

   b Calculate the probability that there are at least 50 letters
      delivered on the following Monday.

   c i   What assumptions have you made in calculating your
          answer to part b?
      ii How reasonable do you think those assumptions are?

S2

1 Of the bolts produced by a factory, 5% are defective.

   a Find the probability that in a box of 20 bolts more than 3 are defective.

   b Using a suitable approximation find the probability that in a box of 250 bolts there will be between 10 and 14 (inclusive) defective bolts.

2 The continuous random variable X has a rectangular distribution with this probability density function, where k is a constant.

$$f(x) = \begin{cases} \dfrac{1}{5} & 8 \leqslant x \leqslant k \\ 0 & \text{otherwise} \end{cases}$$

   a State the value of k.

   b Hence find values for the mean, μ, and the variance, σ^2, of X.

   c Calculate $P(X > \mu + \sigma)$.

3 The Welcome guest house is situated in a seaside town. It has 7 bedrooms available to guests requesting overnight accommodation. The number of these bedrooms requested on a summer's night may be modelled by a Poisson distribution with a mean 5.5.

   a Find the probability that the number of bedrooms requested by guests on a particular summer's night is
      i 7 or fewer   ii exactly 7.

   b The Happy Days Hotel is next door to the Welcome guest house. It has 43 bedrooms available to guests. The number of these bedrooms requested on a summer's night may be modelled by a Poisson distribution with mean 37.

      i Use a suitable approximation to find the probability that on a particular summer's night the number of bedrooms requested at the Happy Days Hotel exceeds the number of bedrooms available.

      ii Explain why the distribution used in part **b i** is not a good model to use for the number of bedrooms occupied in the Happy Days Hotel on a particular summer's night.

4 The number of telephone calls to a sixth form college admissions office is monitored.

a During working hours in February the number of calls follows a Poisson distribution with mean 2 per 15-minute interval. During a particular 15-minute interval, what is:

   i the probability that two or fewer calls are received
   ii the probability that four or more calls are received
   iii the smallest number of calls to be exceeded with probability less than 0.01?

b During June the number of calls received on a weekday follows a Poisson distribution with mean 68. Using a suitable approximation, estimate the probability that on a particular day more than 80 calls are received.

c On any particular working day the number of attempts to telephone the office is distributed at random at a constant average rate. Usually calls are answered immediately. However, for a short period in August, immediately after the publication of GCSE results, the number of calls increases and the telephones are frequently engaged.

   State, giving a reason, whether the Poisson distribution is likely to provide an adequate model for each of these distributions.

   i The number of calls received in each minute during working hours of a day in June.
   ii The number of calls received in each minute during working hours of a day immediately after the publication of GCSE results.
   iii The number of calls received on each working day throughout the year.

5 A golfer practises on a driving range. His objective is to hit a ball to within 10 m of a flag.

a On his first visit the probability of success with each particular ball is 0.3. If he hits ten balls what is the probability of
   i four or fewer successes   ii four or more successes?

b Some weeks later the probability of success has increased to 0.53. What is the probability of 120 or more successes in 250 drives?

c A year later the probability of success has increased to 0.92. What is the probability of 3 or fewer failures in 50 drives?

S2

6 In one of the hospitals in a metropolitan area 30 people are diagnosed with a particular disease over a six-month period. Doctors know from previous research that the probability of a patient recovering from this disease is 0.3. Assuming the patients recover independently of one another

   a find the probability that

      i at least 12 will recover   ii exactly 5 will recover.

   In the whole metropolitan area, 182 people have contracted the disease.

   b Using a suitable approximation, find the probability that the number of people who will recover is between 56 and 76 inclusive.

   c Comment on the assumption of independence.   [(c) Edexcel Limited 1999]

7 A pottery produces large quantities of drinking mugs and knows from past experience that 5% of its production will be classified as 'seconds'.
   A random sample of 20 mugs is taken from the production.

   a Write down an appropriate distribution to model the number of 'seconds' in a sample of size 20.

   b Find the probability that

      i there are exactly 2 'seconds' in the sample
      ii there are more than 4 'seconds' in the sample.

   A random sample of size 150 is taken.

   c Find the probability that the number of 'seconds' in this sample is between 12 and 15 (inclusive), using

      i a Poisson approximation   ii a normal approximation.

   d State why an adjustment had to be made when using the normal approximation.

   Without using an approximation the probability in part c is found to be 0.0704 to 4 decimal places.

   e Comment upon the accuracy of your approximations in part c.   [(c) Edexcel Limited 1999]

8 The number of letters received by Luichan on a weekday may be modelled by a Poisson distribution with mean 3.0.

   a Find the probability that on a particular weekday Luichan receives

      i 4 or fewer letters
      ii exactly 4 letters
      iii 4 or more letters.

   b Find the probability that the total number of letters received by Luichan over a period of three weekdays exceeds 11.

9 **a** Give two conditions which must apply when modelling a random variable by a Poisson distribution.

A particular make of kettle is sold by a shop at an average rate of 5 per week. The random variable X represents the number of kettles sold in any one week and X is modelled by a Poisson distribution. The shop manager notices that at the beginning of a particular week there are 7 kettles in stock.

b Find the probability that the shop will not be able to meet all the demands for kettles that week, assuming that it is not possible to restock during the week.

In order to increase sales performance, the manager decides to have in stock at the beginning of each week sufficient kettles to have at least a 99% chance of being able to meet all demands during that week.

c Find the smallest number of kettles that should be in stock at the beginning of each week.

d Using a suitable approximation find the probability that the shop sells at least 18 kettles in a four-week period, subject to stock always being available to meet demand.

10 Among the blood cells of a certain animal species, the proportion of cells which are of type O is $\frac{1}{3}$ and the proportion of cells which are of type AB is 0.005.

a Find the probability that in a random sample of 8 blood cells at least 2 will be of type O.

Using suitable approximations, find the probability that
b in a random sample of 200 blood cells the total number of type O and type AB cells is at least 81

c in a random sample of 900 blood cells there will be at least 4 cells of type AB.

5

Exit ⟹

Summary

Refer to

○ If a continuous random variable, X, has a uniform distribution over the interval (α, β), then it will have probability density function given by

$$f(x) = \begin{cases} \dfrac{1}{\beta - \alpha} & \alpha \leqslant x \leqslant \beta \\ 0 & \text{otherwise} \end{cases}$$

   ○ median = mean = $E(X) = \dfrac{\alpha + \beta}{2}$

   ○ $Var(X) = \dfrac{(\beta - \alpha)^2}{12}$

5.1

○ If X is a discrete random variable and Y is a continuous random variable which is to be used to approximate X, then you must use the continuity correction

$$P(X = x) \overset{approx}{\approx} P(x - 0.5 < Y < x + 0.5)$$

5.2

○ If $X \sim B(n, p)$ then $E(X) = np$ and $Var(X) = npq = np(1 - p)$.
If n is large and p is close to 0.5 (when both np and $n(1 - p)$ are > 5), so that the distribution is nearly symmetrical, then you can use the normal distribution $N(np, npq)$ to approximate X.

5.2

○ If $X \sim Po(\lambda)$ then $E(X) = \lambda$ and $Var(X) = \lambda$.
If λ is large (>10) then you can use the normal distribution $N(\lambda, \lambda)$ to approximate X.

5.3

Links

Continuous distributions are useful in many situations to model quantities that vary with time or some other continuous variable.

Quantum physics is the study of very small particles and the mechanical systems involving them. These systems interact randomly and therefore involve much uncertainty.
Using probability models, Physicists can gain insight into how particles behave on a near atomic scale.

S2

6

Hypothesis testing

This chapter will show you how to
- use the correct logical structure in carrying out a hypothesis test, and how to identify whether the test should be one- or two- tailed
- find the critical region and the critical values for a hypothesis test
- carry out hypothesis tests for the proportion p in a binomial distribution and for the parameter λ in a Poisson distribution.

Before you start

You should know how to:

1 Calculate probabilities for the binomial distribution using tables.

2 Calculate probabilities for the Poisson distribution using tables.

Check in:

1 If $X \sim B(15, 0.2)$ find the least value of x for which $P(X > x) < 0.05$

2 If $X \sim Po(10)$ find the least value of x for which $P(X < x) < 0.025$

S2

Anil tossed a coin five times and got only 1 head.
He thought the coin was biased.

Vanya tossed another coin 500 times and got 129 heads.
She thought her coin was biased.

Could you argue that either coin was biased?
Or that either coin was not biased?

For Anil's case you can work out the probability distribution exactly as shown in this table:

Number of heads	0	1	2	3	4	5
Probability	0.03125	0.15625	0.3125	0.3125	0.15625	0.03125

The likelihood of getting 0, 1, 4 or 5 heads is 0.375 or $\frac{3}{8}$.

This is less than half, but more than a third, and you would not usually refer to something which happens more often than 1 in 3 times as a 'rare event'.

However, it would not be reasonable to try to argue that this outcome provided positive support for the proposition that the coin was fair. If you tossed a coin which only came up heads 30% of the time then 1 head in 5 tosses would be very common. The best you can say is that Anil's result does not provide convincing evidence that the coin is biased, and be very careful to say this explicitly – never that it provides evidence that the coin is unbiased.

Look for 'at least as extreme a result as the observed'. Unless you have some reason to expect the proportion to be < 0.5 or > 0.5 before you know the outcome, then you should include the extreme results at the other end as well.

In the English legal system only 2 verdicts are allowed – guilty and not guilty. A not guilty verdict does not necessarily mean that the jury were convinced that the accused was innocent. The Scottish legal system has a third verdict 'not proven' which means it is more reasonable for a person found not guilty in Scotland to claim they were found innocent by the court.

Vanya's observation in her experiment actually has a higher proportion of heads than Anil's, but with a large number of trials the proportion seen is much more likely to be close to the probability and the likelihood of seeing this with a fair coin is almost vanishingly small.

What happens if the situation is not as clear-cut as either of these?

S2

How do you decide what to class as a 'rare event' and how to talk about what the observation means?

The null hypothesis, H_0, is the probability basis under which the test is to be considered. So for the coin-tossing example this would be H_0: $p = \frac{1}{2}$ and the alternative hypothesis, H_1: $p \neq \frac{1}{2}$ in this case, is what you would turn to if you felt there was convincing evidence that H_0 was not true.

To decide if an event is 'rare', you compare where the value of an observed statistic lies within the sampling distribution under the null hypothesis. The significance level of the test is the limit at which you would judge the event to be 'rare'.

> If the event observed is not an unusual occurrence when the null hypothesis is true, it will also not be unusual for a lot of other situations, so to say that you accept the null hypothesis is a very weak statement. In such situations, it is safer to say that there is insufficient evidence to be able to reject H_0. Take care with the language you use in your conclusion.

S2

To construct a hypothesis test:

- identify formally the null and alternative hypotheses. The null hypothesis, H_0, will be in the form
    $$H_0: p = \quad \text{or} \quad H_0: \lambda =$$
  The alternative hypothesis, H_1, will be in the form
    $$H_1: p < \quad \text{or} \quad p > \quad \text{for a one-tailed test or}$$
    $$H_1: p \neq \quad \quad \quad \text{for a two-tailed test.}$$
- State the significance level you are using to test your null hypothesis.
- Apply your significance level to the result of your test. Your conclusion should be that either
    - there is not sufficient evidence to reject the null hypothesis at this level, or
    - there is sufficient evidence to reject the null hypothesis in favour of the alternative hypothesis at the given significance level.
  You must state your conclusions in the context of the given problem.

If you are told that the sample was discovered not to be random, then the conclusion of your test is not valid.

EXAMPLE 1

The proportion of applications from women to a particular course has been stable at 35% over a number of years. The course is revised.
A random sample of 50 applications is taken to see if the proportion of women applying for the new course has changed.

a Give the null and alternative hypotheses you would use in the test.

b In fact 31 out of the 50 applications in the test were from women, and the null hypothesis was rejected at the 5% level of significance. State the conclusion in context.

---

a $H_0: p = 0.35$ *vs* $H_1: p \neq 0.35$

b Reject H_0 and conclude there is sufficient evidence at the 5% level to suggest that the proportion of applications from women is not 35%.

In part **a** you are only looking at whether the proportion has changed. The revision might make it more or less attractive to women.

EXAMPLE 2

The number of bikes going over the speed limit on a road in a housing estate in a 10-minute period between 4 p.m. and 7 p.m. may be modelled by a Poisson random variable with parameter 2.2. Sleeping policemen (traffic humps) are installed on the road as a traffic-calming measure.

a Give the null and alternative hypotheses you would use in a test to see if the number of bikes breaking the speed limit on the road has been reduced.

b In a randomly selected 10-minute period between 4 p.m. and 7 p.m. after the change was made there were two bikes breaking the speed limit, and the null hypothesis was not rejected at the 5% level of significance.
State this conclusion in context.

---

a $H_0: \lambda = 2.2$ *vs* $H_1: \lambda < 2.2$

b There is insufficient evidence to reject H_0 at the 5% level. You can not conclude that the average number of bikes breaking the speed limit in a 10-minute period has been reduced.

In part **a** you are only looking at whether the average rate has been reduced.

Exercise 6.1

1 The proportion of primary school teachers who have passed
   A-level Maths is 23%. The government launch a campaign to
   encourage people with A-level Maths to consider teaching in
   primary schools.

   A random sample of 40 applications for training is taken to see
   if the proportion of people with A-level Maths has increased.
   Give the null and alternative hypotheses you would use in the test.

2 In the test in question **1**, 13 out of the 40 applications were from people
   with A-level Maths, and the null hypothesis was not rejected at the
   5% level of significance. State the conclusion in context.

3 The number of accidents on a particular stretch of road can be modeled
   by a Poisson distribution with a mean of 0.45 accidents per day on weekdays.

   a Give the null and alternative hypotheses you would use in a test to
         see if the number of accidents on that stretch of road is different at
         the weekend.

   Over a month which has 8 weekend days in it there were 7 accidents
   recorded on that stretch of road, and the null hypothesis was rejected
   at the 5% level of significance.

   b State the conclusion in context.

4 If, in the situation given in question **2**, a random sample had shown that
   16 out of the 40 applications were from people with A-level Maths,
   and the null hypothesis *was* rejected at the 5% level of significance,
   state the conclusion in context.

5 In a random sample taken for the situations in question **4**, 5 accidents
   were recorded on that stretch of road, and the null hypothesis over the
   month *was not* rejected at the 5% level of significance.
   State the conclusion in context.

In a hypothesis test, the extreme part of the sampling distribution is known as the critical region. The significance level of the test gives the size of this region. The conclusion of the test is to reject H_0 if the observed values lie in the critical region. The common default significance level is 5%, but you may be told to use other levels.

> A smaller significance level means that you are
> - less likely to reject H_0 incorrectly
> - more likely to be unable to reject H_0 when it is untrue.
>
> A larger significance level means that
> - you are more likely to be able to reject H_0 when it is untrue but you are also more likely to reject H_0 when it is true.

Similarly, in a court trial, less evidence means that you are less likely to be able to convict even if the defendant is guilty.

To increase the effectiveness of a test without changing the significance level, you can increase the sample size.
This however means that the test is going to cost more.

Null hypothesis H_0: $\lambda = 7.5$

Consider the case where the Poisson distribution is appropriate, and the null hypothesis is that $\lambda = 7.5$. The sampling distribution looks like this:

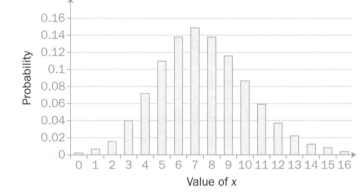

If you wanted to test that the parameter was different from 7.5, then very low or very high observed values would be considered 'extreme' and would push you away from the null hypothesis. This would be a two-tailed test, because values in both tails of the distribution would be considered extreme.

Alternative hypothesis H_1: $\lambda \neq 7.5$

At the 5% level of significance, the two-tailed test will reject H_0 if X is 0, 1 or 2 or if it is 14 or more. There is a probability of 2.0% at the bottom end and another 2.2% at the top end, which is as close to 5% as it is possible to get.

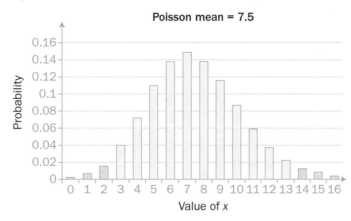

Poisson mean = 7.5

For a two-tailed test at the 5% level of significance you want to find values c_1 and c_2 such that $P(X \leqslant c_1) \leqslant 0.025$ and $P(X \geqslant c_2) \leqslant 0.025$ to define the critical region.

Alternative hypothesis H_1: $\lambda < 7.5$

If you had some reason to expect that λ would be lower than 7.5 if it was anything, then only very low observed values would be considered 'extreme' – so this would be a one-tailed test.

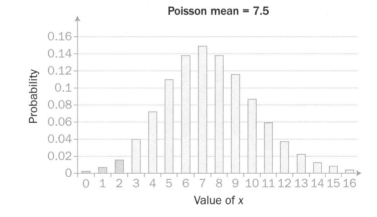

Poisson mean = 7.5

At the 5% level of significance, the one-tailed test will reject H_0 if X is 0, 1 or 2. There is a probability of 2.0% of rejecting H_0 when it is in fact true, which is as close to 5% as it is possible to get. If the value 3 was included, then this probability would rise to 5.9% which is greater than 5%.

For a one-tailed test at the 5% level of significance you want to find the value c such that

$$P(X \leqslant c) \leqslant 0.05 \quad \text{if} \quad H_1 \text{ contains} <$$
$$\text{or} \quad P(X \geqslant c) \leqslant 0.05 \quad \text{if} \quad H_1 \text{ contains} >$$

to define the critical region.

S2

Alternative hypothesis $H_1: \lambda > 7.5$

Use this hypothesis if you expect that the mean is higher if anything.

The one-tailed test at the upper end has a critical region of X being 13 or more, which has a probability of 4.3%. Including 12 would give a probability of 7.9% which is greater than the 5% significance level.

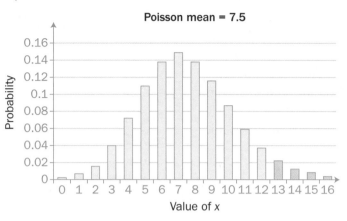

Poisson mean = 7.5

How to use the probability tables to find the critical region

Now consider the $B(15, 0.5)$ distribution. The table shows both the individual probabilities and the cumulative probabilities, and the graph shows the shape of the distribution.

x	$P(X = x)$	$P(X \leqslant x)$
0	0.00003	0.00003
1	0.00046	0.00049
2	0.00320	0.00369
3	0.01389	0.01758
4	0.04166	0.05923
5	0.09164	0.15088
6	0.15274	0.30362
7	0.19638	0.50000
8	0.19638	0.69638
9	0.15274	0.84912
10	0.09164	0.94077
11	0.04166	0.98242
12	0.01389	0.99631
13	0.00320	0.99951
14	0.00046	0.99997
15	0.00003	1.00000

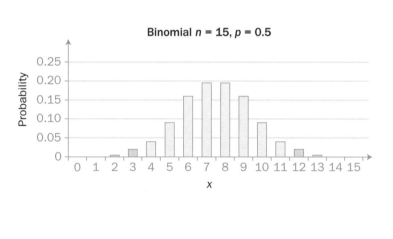

Binomial $n = 15$, $p = 0.5$

While the individual probabilities are helpful in understanding the shape of the distribution and getting a sense of where the extreme values will be, it is the table of cumulative values which allows you to find the critical region easily.

You could be asked to do a hypothesis test for which you would have to calculate the probabilities as well because they are not in the tables.

When working with a discrete distribution you will normally not be able to get exactly the significance level you are aiming for – so use the critical region which gives the closest possible to the target (this should be more extreme than the target unless you are told that the significance level has to be no more than $x\%$).

Here a 5%, two-tailed test would include 0–3 at the bottom, and at the top end the rest of the critical region will be 12–15. The cumulative probabilities up to 3 ($= 0.01758$) and up to 11 ($= 0.98242$) are highlighted in the table.

The exact level
($0.01758 + (1 - 0.98242) = 3.5\%$) is the closest achievable value less than 5%.

A 5% one-tailed test for a decrease in p would have critical region 0–3 (with an exact value of 1.8% being the closest possible value less than 5%).

Hypothesis tests are more effective when you are working with continuous distributions (in which case you can have a critical region giving exactly the probability you want) or discrete distributions with larger numbers of possible values.

The Poisson distribution is not symmetric, nor is any binomial distribution where p is not 0.5, and in these cases you need to do each tail separately with a target of half the level of significance for each.

This table and graph show the B(15, 0.2) distribution:

x	$P(X = x)$	$P(X \leqslant x)$
0	0.03518	0.03518
1	0.13194	0.16713
2	0.23090	0.39802
3	0.25014	0.64816
4	0.18760	0.83577
5	0.10318	0.93895
6	0.04299	0.98194
7	0.01382	0.99576
8	0.00345	0.99922
9	0.00067	0.99989
10	0.00010	0.99999
11	0.00001	1.00000
12	0.00000	1.00000
13	0.00000	1.00000
14	0.00000	1.00000
15	0.00000	1.00000

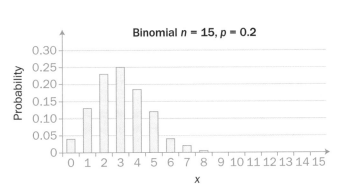

S2

Since $P(X = 0) = 0.035$, a two-tailed test at the 5% level of significance will have a critical region of 0 at the bottom (with probability of 3.5%) and >6 (i.e. 7–15) at the top (with probability $1 - 0.99576 = 0.4\%$). The actual total probability of rejecting H_0 when it was true would be 3.9%.

Summary

o The null hypothesis, H_0, gives parameter values which are used to produce the sampling distribution against which the observed values are compared.

o The alternative hypothesis, H_1, identifies whether a one- or two- tailed test is needed. One-tailed tests look only for p (or λ) to have increased or decreased, and this must not be just because the observation was high or was low. If there was no reason to expect the shift to be in a particular direction without looking at the observed data then a two-tailed test would be used.

o The critical region for a test is the set of values for which the null hypothesis will be rejected. The critical value(s) are the boundary values of the critical region i.e. the first value at either end for which H_0 would be rejected.

o Significance level = size of a hypothesis test = probability of rejecting H_0 when it was actually true.

o You must state a clear conclusion, referring to the context of the example.

Exercise 6.2

For the following hypothesis tests, state whether you should use a one- or two- tailed test, and find the critical region. Also state the exact significance level for the critical region in each case.

Use the tables of probabilities at the back of the book.

1 For a binomial distribution with $n = 20$, testing

   a H_0: $p = 0.5$ against H_1: $p \neq 0.5$ with a 5% level of significance

   b H_0: $p = 0.5$ against H_1: $p < 0.5$ with a 5% level of significance

   c H_0: $p = 0.5$ against H_1: $p \neq 0.5$ with a 2% level of significance.

S2

2 For a binomial distribution with $n = 50$, testing
H_0: $p = 0.3$ against H_1: $p \neq 0.3$
with a 5% level of significance.

3 For a binomial distribution with $n = 40$, testing
H_0: $p = 0.8$ against H_1: $p \neq 0.8$
with a 5% level of significance.

4 For a Poisson distribution, testing
$H_0 : \lambda = 8$ against $H_1 : \lambda \neq 8$
with a 5% level of significance.

5 For a Poisson distribution, testing
$H_0 : \lambda = 9.5$ against $H_1 : \lambda > 9.5$
with a 5% level of significance.

6 For a Poisson distribution, testing
$H_0 : \lambda = 8.5$ against $H_1 : \lambda < 8.5$
with a 1% level of significance.

7 For a Poisson distribution, testing
$H_0 : \lambda = 6$ against $H_1 : \lambda > 6$
with a 10% level of significance.

S2

You can apply a hypothesis test to a binomial distribution.

The conclusions will be in one of these forms:
- There is sufficient evidence to reject H_0 in favour of H_1 at the given significance level.
- There is not sufficient evidence to reject H_0 at the given significance level.

  Your conclusion should refer to the context of the question.

This is a lack of evidence against the hypothesis, not evidence in support of it. Your language must reflect this.

EXAMPLE 1

30% of customers in a large store present the store's loyalty card when they buy something in the store.
The store runs an advertising campaign to promote their loyalty card.
After the advertising campaign has finished, a random sample of 30 sales is examined and it was found that a loyalty card was used in 15 of them.
Test at the 5% level of significance whether the campaign has been effective in increasing the use of the loyalty card.

Let X = the number of sales where a loyalty card is used.
Then $X \sim B(30, p)$.
This is a one-tailed test since it is looking for p to be increased from 0.3.
The formal statement of the hypotheses is
$H_0: p = 0.3 \qquad H_1: p > 0.3$

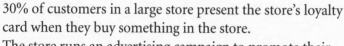
Look at the cumulative distribution function for the B(30, 0.3) distribution:
$F(12) = 0.9155, \quad F(13) = 0.9599$
For a 5% test, the critical value is 14
(giving an exact value of 4.01%).
The first value for which the null hypothesis would be rejected is if loyalty cards were used in 14 of the 30 sales.

There were actually 15 cards used, so the decision is to reject H_0.
Here, you could conclude:
Reject H_0. There is significant evidence (at the 5% level) to suggest that the advertising campaign has increased the use of the store loyalty card.

You are looking at the probability of 'as extreme (or more) than the critical value' so here
$P(X \geqslant 14) = 1 - P(X < 13)$
$\qquad\qquad = 0.0401$

Make a clear conclusion. Refer to the significance level and the context of the example.

S2

EXAMPLE 2

A psychologist moves to New Zealand after working in the UK. In the UK 25% of her patients suffered from a fear of heights.

In a random sample of 40 of her patients in New Zealand she finds that there are 13 who suffer from a fear of heights.

Test at the 5% level of significance whether there is a difference in the proportions of people who suffer from a fear of heights in the UK and in New Zealand.

The psychologist has no reason to suppose that the proportion should be higher or lower in New Zealand than in the UK.

This should be a two-tailed test looking for a difference.

> Do *not* think that because '13 out of 40 is greater than 25%' it is a one-tailed test for an increase.

The formal statement of the hypotheses is

H_0: $p = 0.25$ H_1: $p \neq 0.25$

Look at the cumulative distribution function for the $B(40, 0.25)$ distribution:

$F(4) = 0.0160$

$F(5) = 0.0433$

$F(14) = 0.9456$

$F(15) = 0.9738$

so the closest you can get to a 5% test (2.5% at either end) is to use 4 and 16 as the critical values.

Reject H_0 if $X \leqslant 4$ or $X \geqslant 16$

The exact value of the test is actually $1.6\% + 2.6\% = 4.2\%$

Since there are 13 patients in the sample who suffer from a fear of heights, this is not significant, and H_0 is not rejected.

The formal conclusion is:

There is not sufficient evidence to reject H_0 at the 5% level. It is not clear that there is a difference in the proportion of people who suffer from a fear of heights in the UK and in New Zealand.

EXAMPLE 3

The proportion of 15-year-old boys drinking alcohol at least once a month in Ireland in 2004 was 60%.
The government introduced a new alcohol awareness education programme to try to reduce the level of under-age drinking.
A random sample of forty 15-year-old boys was taken during the evaluation of the effectiveness of the programme, and 21 of them were drinking alcohol at least once a month.
Carry out a test, using a 5% level of significance, and advise on the effectiveness of the programme in reducing the proportion of 15-year-old boys drinking alcohol.

This is a one-tailed test since it is looking for p to be reduced from 0.6.
Let X be the number of boys in the sample drinking alcohol at least once a month.
Then $X \sim B(40, p)$.

State the null and alternative hypotheses carefully, and identify the rest of the distribution.

The hypotheses are:
$H_0: p = 0.6 \quad H_1: p < 0.6$

There are no tabulated values for $p = 0.6$, so you need to consider the number of boys who do *not* drink alcohol at least once a month and use the $n = 40$, $p = 0.4$ table.

*Let y be the number of boys in the sample who do **not** drink alcohol at least once a month.*
Then $y \sim B(40, p)$
The hypotheses are now
$H_0: p = 0.4 \quad H_1: p > 0.4$

Extreme values will be found at the top end. Large numbers of boys who do not drink alcohol at least once a month push you away from the null hypothesis that there has been no improvement.

Number of boys not drinking	19	20	21	22	23	24
Cumulative probability	0.870	0.926	0.961	0.981	0.992	0.997

For a 5% test, you have a critical region of 22 or more in the sample who do not drink alcohol at least once a month (with an exact value of 3.9%).

This means that you need fewer than 18 in the sample who do drink alcohol at least once a month in order to reject the null hypothesis.

$40 - 22 = 18$

Conclude that you cannot reject H_0. There is insufficient evidence at the 5% level of significance to suggest that the programme has reduced the proportion of 15-year-old boys who drink alcohol at least once a month.

S2

Exercise 6.3

1 A newspaper headline in France stated 'Majority would vote for President'. The article explained that in a survey of 50 randomly selected people, 27 had said that they would vote for the President. The leader of the opposition party wrote to the newspaper and said that such evidence was inconclusive, and according to standard statistical techniques, the result was consistent with only 40% of the whole population voting for the President. The newspaper editor stated that the results showed that 40% was too low.

Stating the null and alternative hypothesis, test at the 5% level which of them was justified in his claim.

2 In a multiple choice examination paper in Psychology, a candidate has to select which one of five possible answers to a question is correct. On a paper of 40 questions she gets 13 correct answers.

Her teacher says she can't have done any work at all. Test, at the 5% level, whether there is evidence to suggest that she has done better than just guessing.

3 From past records a manufacturer of plastic garden gnomes knows that 20% of them will have defects. To monitor the production process, a random sample of 25 gnomes is checked each day and the number of gnomes with defects is recorded.

Find the critical region for a two-tailed test at the 5% level of significance of the hypothesis that the probability that a gnome has defects is 0.20. State the actual value of the test.

4 The proportion of bits received incorrectly when a digital signal is transmitted under normal conditions is 5%.
A digital signal consisting of 50 bits is transmitted during a thunderstorm. Six of the bits are received incorrectly.

Test at the 5% level of significance whether the proportion of bits received incorrectly is higher than normal during a thunderstorm.

S2

You use the same process for testing the Poisson distribution:

- identify the hypotheses formally and define the critical region
- carry out the test
- state conclusions.

EXAMPLE 1

A single observation x is to be taken from a Poisson distribution with parameter λ. This observation is to be used to test $H_0: \lambda = 5.5$ against $H_1: \lambda \neq 5.5$.

a Using a 5% significance level, find the critical region for this test. State the exact level of your test.

The actual value of x obtained was 3.

b State a conclusion that can be drawn based on this value.

---

a $F(1) = 0.0266$ is the closest to 2.5% at the bottom end.
$F(11) = 0.9890$ gives the closest overall value to 5%.
So the critical region is $X \leqslant 1$ or $X \geqslant 11$.
The exact size of the test is $0.0266 + (1 - 0.9890) = 0.0376$

c Since 3 is not in the critical region, you cannot reject H_0. There is not sufficient evidence at the 5% level to suggest that the mean is not 5.5.

EXAMPLE 2

The number of accidents on a stretch of road may be modelled by a Poisson distribution with an average rate of 2.5 accidents per week.

a Find the probability that there are at least 5 accidents in a randomly chosen week.

Some new warning notices are installed and in a three-week period there are 4 accidents.

b Using a 5% significance level, test whether there has been a reduction in the average rate of occurrence of accidents.

---

a Use the Po(2.5) tables:
$P(X \geqslant 5) = 1 - P(X \leqslant 4) = 1 - 0.8912 = 0.1088$

b Test $H_0: \lambda = 7.5$ against $H_1: \lambda < 7.5$ For the three-week period the mean is $3 \times 2.5 = 7.5$ under H_0.

$F(2) = 0.0203$, which is the closest to 5%, so the test will be to reject H_0 if no more than 2 accidents occur in the three-week period.

Since there were 4 accidents you cannot reject H_0. You conclude that there is insufficient evidence at the 5% level to suggest that the mean rate of occurrences has been reduced.

Exercise 6.4

1 A single observation x is to be taken from a Poisson distribution with parameter λ. This observation is to be used to test $H_0 : \lambda = 9.5$ against $H_1 : \lambda \neq 9.5$.

   a Using a 5% significance level, find the critical region for this test. State the exact level of your test.

   The actual value of x obtained was 4.

   b State a conclusion that can be drawn based on this value.

2 Accidents occur at a certain road junction at the average of 3 per month.

   a Suggest a suitable model for the number of accidents at the junction in the next month.

   b Find the probability of 2 or more accidents at this road junction in the next month.

   The local residents have applied for a crossing to be installed. The planning committee agree to monitor the situation for the next 12 months. If there is at least one month with 5 or more accidents in it they will install a crossing.

   c Find the probability that a crossing is installed.

   d If a crossing is installed, and the local residents want to see if there is any improvement in the situation, give the critical region which would apply if the test was to look at the number of accidents in:
      i a one-month period   ii a three-month period.

   e Give one advantage of choosing the
      i one-month test period   ii three-month test period.

3 'Hits' on a World Wide Web page at a particular location on the Internet occur at an average rate of one every three minutes, between the times 1100 and 1600.

   a Which distribution is appropriate to model this situation and why?

   b Calculate an approximation for the probability that there are more than 30 'hits' in an hour between 1100 and 1600.

   c Why might the probability that there are more than 30 'hits' in the hour 0300 to 0400 be different from the answer in part b?

   d If there were 4 hits between 0330 and 0400, test at the 5% level of significance that there is a difference in the average rate of occurrences between 1100 to 1600 and 0300 to 0400.

1 At a recent general election, Hollyoaks Primary School was used as a polling station.

    a The number of voters arriving at the polling station on the morning of election day could be modelled by a Poisson distribution with mean of 1.5 per 5-minute interval.

        i Find the probability that in a particular 5-minute interval the number of voters arriving was 2 or fewer.

        ii Use an appropriate distributional approximation to find the probability that the number of voters arriving during a particular *hour* exceeded 20.

    b The number of voters arriving between 6 p.m. and 9 p.m. could also be modelled by a Poisson distribution, but the arrival rate could differ from the morning arrival rate. During the half hour from 6.30 p.m. to 7 p.m. 18 voters arrived.

    Test, at the 5% level of significance, whether the arrival rate between 6 p.m. and 9 p.m. is higher than the rate during the morning.

2 A mill produces cloth in 80-metre lengths. It is common for lengths to contain faults that have to be treated before the cloth is sold. These faults are distributed over the cloth independently, at random and at a constant average rate.

    a Name a distribution that will provide a suitable model for the number of faults in an 80-metre length of cloth.

    b A new manager states that it is unacceptable for the mean number of faults per 80-metre length of cloth to exceed 2. The next 80-metre length of cloth produced contains 5 faults.

    Carry out a hypothesis test, using the 5% significance level, to test the hypothesis that the mean number of faults per 80-metre length cloth does not exceed 2.

    c The results of the test are presented to the new manager, who states that a significance level of 5% is too high and that a level of 1% should be used in order to reduce the possibility of error.

    Without carrying out any further calculations, comment on the new manager's statement.

[(c) Edexcel Limited 1998]

3 A manufacturer of windows has used a process which produced flaws in the glass randomly at a rate of 0.6 per m^2. In an attempt to reduce the number of flaws produced, a new process is tried out. A randomly chosen window produced using this new process has an area of 7 m^2 and contains only 1 flaw.
Stating your hypotheses clearly, test at the 10% level of significance whether or not the rate of occurrence of flaws using the new procedure has decreased.

4 In a multiple choice examination paper in Biology, a candidate has to select which one of four possible answers to a question is correct.
On a paper of 50 questions she gets 19 correct answers.

Her teacher says she can't have done any work at all. Test, at the 5% level, whether there is evidence to suggest that she has done better than just guessing.

5 A single observation x is to be taken from a Poisson distribution with parameter λ.
This observation is to be used to test $H_0 : \lambda = 7$ against $H_1 : \lambda \neq 7$.

   a Using a 5% significance level, find the critical region for this test assuming that the probability of rejection in either tail is as close as possible to 2.5%.

   b Write down the significance level of this test.

   The actual value of x obtained was 5.
   c State a conclusion that can be drawn based on this value.   [(c) Edexcel Limited 2003]

6 A manufacturer of sheet metal has used a process which produced flaws in the metal randomly at a rate of 0.3 per m^2. In an attempt to reduce the number of flaws, a new process is tried out.
A randomly chosen window produced using this new process has an area of 8 m^2 and contains only 1 flaw.

Stating your hypotheses clearly, test at the 10% level of significance whether or not the rate of occurrence of flaws has decreased when the new procedure is used.

7 A large office introduced a new procedure to try and ensure that staff shut down their computers over the weekend as an energy saving measure. A recent survey of the staff suggested that in only 35% of cases did the staff do this. In the first weekend following the introduction of this new procedure a random sample of 30 members of staff was taken and in 17 cases they had shut their computer down over the weekend.

   a Stating your hypotheses clearly test, at the 5% level of significance, whether or not there is evidence that the new procedure has been successful.

A secretary complained that this sample did not give a true picture of the effectiveness of the new procedure.

   b Explain briefly why the secretary's claim might be justified and suggest how a more effective check on the new procedure could be made.

8 In a multiple choice examination paper in Physics, a candidate has to select which one of four possible answers to a question is correct. On a paper of 50 questions he gets 16 correct answers.

His teacher says he can't have done any work at all. Test, at the 5% level, whether there is evidence to suggest that he has done better than just guessing.

9 A single observation x is to be taken from a Poisson distribution with parameter λ. This observation is to be used to test $H_0: \lambda = 9$ against $H_1: \lambda < 9$.

   a Using a 5% significance level, find the critical region for this test.

   b Write down the significance level of this test.

The actual value of x obtained was 5.

   c State a conclusion that can be drawn based on this value.

10 A farmer is studying the behaviour of sheep in a large field. The field is divided into a number of equally sized squares and the average number of sheep per square is 3.5. The sheep are randomly spread throughout the field.

a Suggest a suitable model for the number of sheep in a square and give a suitable value for any parameter or parameters required.

Calculate the probability that a randomly selected square contains

b no sheep

c more than 5 sheep.

A sheep dog has been sent into the field to round up the sheep.

d Explain why the model may be no longer applicable.

In another field the number of sheep in a randomly selected square of the same size is 7.

e Test, at the 1% level of significance, whether the average number of sheep in a square in this field is higher than in the first field.

6

Exit ⟹

Summary

Refer to

- The null hypothesis will be in the form H_0: $p =$ or H_0: $\lambda =$ and the alternative hypothesis is in one of the forms H_1: $p >$ or $p <$ or $p \neq$ (or similar for the Poisson).

  - If the alternative hypothesis is $\lambda \neq$ or $p \neq$ then the test is two-tailed. The other forms give a one-tailed test.

  - The significance level of the test is the probability that a test will reject the null hypothesis when it is actually true.

  - Conclusions for a hypothesis need to refer to the evidence – there is evidence to suggest the null hypothesis is false, or a lack of evidence to suggest it is false (when the null can not be rejected). It is important that conclusions do not imply something has been proved, nor that there is positive evidence in support of the null hypothesis.

    6.1

- The critical region for a hypothesis test is the set of values for which the null hypothesis will be rejected. The critical value(s) are the boundary value(s) of the critical region.

    6.2

- You carry out hypothesis tests for the binomial and Poisson distributions by comparing the observed value with the cumulative distribution function specified in the null hypothesis (often by using a table of probabilities).

    6.3–6.4

Links

Many areas of modern life routinely use statistical testing to make decisions about what constitutes unusual behaviour or to decide when an outcome deviates from what would be expected. The consequences of not having this understanding can be very costly.

Governments can use hypothesis tests to check the effectiveness of new policies, such as tracking what quantity of waste the average household is recycling, and to monitor statistics related to, for example, crime and healthcare.

S2

1 An engineer measures, to the nearest cm, the lengths of metal rods.
   a Suggest a suitable model to represent the difference between the true lengths and the measured lengths.

   b Find the probability that for a randomly chosen rod the measured length will be within 0.2 cm of the true length.

   Two rods are chosen at random.

   c Find the probability that for both rods the measured lengths will be within 0.2 cm of their true lengths. [(c) Edexcel Limited 2003]

2 A bag contains a large number of coins. Half of them are 1p coins, one third are 2p coins and the remainder are 5p coins.
   a Find the mean and variance of the value of the coins.

   A random sample of 2 coins is chosen from the bag.

   b List all the possible samples that can be drawn.

   c Find the sampling distribution of the mean value of these samples. [(c) Edexcel Limited 2006]

3 The manager of a leisure club is considering a change to the club rules. The club has a large membership and the manager wants to take the views of the members into consideration before deciding whether or not to make the change.
   a Explain briefly why the manager might prefer to use a sample survey rather than a census to obtain the views.

   b Suggest a suitable sampling frame.

   c Identify the sampling units. [(c) Edexcel Limited 2002]

4 A random sample $X_1, X_2, ..., X_n$ is taken from a finite population. A statistic Y is based on this sample.
   a Explain what you understand by the term 'a statistic Y'.

   b Give an example of a statistic.

   c Explain what you understand by the sampling distribution of Y. [(c) Edexcel Limited 2002]

5 Before introducing a new rule, the secretary of a golf club decided to find out how members might react to this rule.
   a Explain why the secretary decided to take a random sample of club members rather than ask all the members.

   b Suggest a suitable sampling frame.

   c Identify the sampling units. [(c) Edexcel Limited 2006]

S2

6 A questionnaire given to a group of employees contained these questions.

   a   What is your age?

   b   Are you male or female?

   c   Are you full-time or part-time?

   d   How many days off sick have you had in last 12 months?

   e   How do you normally travel to work?

   f   What is your annual basic salary?

Which answers would be *qualitative* and which *quantitative*?

7 State whether the following variables are discrete or continuous.

   a   The speed of an aircraft at take-off.

   b   The number of passengers on the aircraft.

   c   The weight of the luggage being carried.

   d   The rate of fuel consumption of the aircraft.

Give reasons for your answers.

8 Use the binomial, Poisson or normal distributions according to which you think is the most appropriate in each of these cases. In each draw attention to any feature of the situation described which supports, or casts doubt on, the suitability of the model you have chosen.
Indicate, where appropriate, that you are using one distribution as an approximation to another.

   a   In a country the mean number of deaths per year from lightning strike is 3.5.

       What is the probability that
       i   in a particular year there are two deaths
       ii   there are less than 6 deaths in a two-year period?

   b   In a town where 45% of people are known to support the government stance on asylum seekers, a television reporter chooses six people to interview on Main Street.
What is the probability that exactly two of them support the government?

   c   A machine produces 14% of items which are too long to be used, and which need to be trimmed. In a batch of 400 items what is the probability that fewer than 50 need to be trimmed?

9 The demand for boxes of sweets at a local shop may be modelled by a Poisson distribution with mean of 2.5 per day.

 a   Find the probability of demand exceeding 3 on a particular day.

The shopkeeper is soon to depart for a three-week holiday, leaving the shop to be managed by her son. The shop is open every day and the shopkeeper wishes to obtain sufficient stock, before she departs, to cater for demand during her absence.

 b   Use a suitable approximation to estimate

  i   the probability that demand for boxes of chocolates during the three-week period will exceed 60

  ii   the minimum number of boxes of chocolates she needs to have in stock to ensure that the probability of demand exceeding stock during the three-week period is less than 0.01.

10 The random variables R, S and T are distributed as follows
$$R \sim B(15, 0.3), \quad S \sim Po(7.5), \quad T \sim N(8, 2^2)$$

Find   a $P(R = 5)$

    b $P(S = 5)$

    c $P(T = 5)$.   [(c) Edexcel Limited 2005]

11 For a particular type of plant 45% have white flowers and the remainder have coloured flowers.
Gardenmania sells plants in batches of 12.
A batch is selected at random.

 a   Calculate the probability that this batch contains
  i   exactly 5 plants with white flowers
  ii   more plants with white flowers than coloured ones.

Gardenmania takes a random sample of 10 batches of plants.

 b   Find the probability that exactly 3 of these batches contain more plants with white flowers than coloured ones.

Due to an increasing demand for these plants by large companies, Gardenmania decides to sell them in batches of 50.

 c   Use a suitable approximation to calculate the probability that a batch of 50 plants contains more than 25 plants with white flowers.   [(c) Edexcel Limited 2007]

S2

12 A drinks machine dispenses lemonade into cups. It is electronically controlled to cut off the flow of lemonade randomly between 180 ml and 200 ml. The random variable X is the volume of lemonade dispensed into a cup.

   a Specify the probability density function of X and sketch its graph.

   b Find the probability that the machine dispenses

      i less than 183 ml

      ii exactly 183 ml.

   c Calculate the inter-quartile range of X.

   d Determine the value of x such that $P(X \geqslant x) = 2P(X \leqslant x)$

   e Interpret in words your value of x.   [(c) Edexcel Limited 2003]

13 The continuous random variable L represents the error, in mm, made when a machine cuts rods to a target length. The distribution of L is continuous and uniform over the interval $[-4.0, 4.0]$.

   Find   **a** $P(L < -2.6)$

           b $P(L < -3.0$ or $L > 3.0)$

   A random sample of 20 rods cut by the machine was checked.

   c Find the probability that more than half of them were within 3.0 mm of the target length.   [(c) Edexcel Limited 2006]

14 A tour operator organises a visit for cricket enthusiasts to India in November. The package includes a ticket for a one-day international in Nagpur. Places on the tour must be booked two months in advance.

From past experience, the tour operator knows that the probability of a person who has booked a place subsequently withdrawing is 0.1 and is independent of other withdrawals.

   a Twenty-five people book places.
      Find the probability that none withdraws.

   b The tour operator only has 21 tickets available for the one-day international. What is the probability that he will be able to provide everyone who goes on tour with a ticket?

   c An organiser of a similar but larger tour accepts 250 bookings but has only 210 tickets for the one-day international.
      Find, using a suitable approximation, the probability that this organiser will be able to provide everyone on this tour with a ticket. (Assume that the probability of a person withdrawing remains at 0.1.)

15 The continuous random variable X has the rectangular distribution given by

$$f(x) = \begin{cases} \frac{1}{5} & -1 \leqslant x \leqslant 4 \\ 0 & \text{otherwise} \end{cases}$$

  a Find the mean and variance of X.

  b Find $P(|X - \mu| > \sigma)$ where μ is the mean and σ is the standard deviation of X.

16 The continuous random variable X has a rectangular distribution.
The mean of X is 7 and the variance of X is 144.
Find **a** the minimum value of X

       b $P(X > 5)$.

17 In a large scale trial of a new drug, it is found that 15% of patients
suffer some mild side-effects and another 0.2% of the patients suffer
a severe side-effect.

  a In a random sample of 20 of the patients, what is the probability that
    i more than 4 of them suffered some mild side-effects
    ii exactly two of them suffered some mild side-effects?

  b Five random samples of 20 patients was taken. What is the probability
    that none of these samples had more than 4 of them suffering some
    mild side-effects?

  c Use a suitable approximation to estimate the probability that none
    of the 100 patients in the samples in part **b** suffered a severe side-effect.

  d A random sample of 300 patients is to be sent a questionnaire.
    Use a suitable approximation to estimate the probability that
    the questionnaire will be sent to more than 50 patients who
    suffered any side-effects.

18 The continuous random variable X has the rectangular distribution given by

$$f(x) = \begin{cases} \frac{1}{4} & 0 \leqslant x \leqslant 4 \\ 0 & \text{otherwise} \end{cases}$$

  a Find $P(X < 1)$.

  b A random sample of 10 observations of X is taken.
    Find the probability that $X < 1$ in not more than 3 of the sample.

  c A random sample of 100 observations of X is taken.
    Use a suitable approximation to estimate the probability
    that $X < 1$ in not more than 30 of this sample.

19 The number of babies born in a maternity unit can be modelled
by a Poisson distribution with an average rate of 3.2 births per day.

    a Find the probability that on a given day there are
        i   exactly 2 births
        ii   not more than 2 births.

    b Use a suitable approximation to estimate the probability that
there are more than 25 births in a particular week.

    c Do you think the number of births in this maternity unit on
January 1st 2000 could be modelled by this Poisson distribution?
Give a reason for your answer.

20 A weather analyst was looking at the distribution of flash floods
in a particular area. She modelled the number of flash floods in
a year as a Poisson random variable. She wished to test the null
hypothesis that the parameter of the distribution was 6 against
the alternative hypothesis that it was greater than 6. She intended
to make one observation, and decided that the critical region
would be 10 or greater.

    a What significance level did she use to get this critical region?

In fact, the value of the parameter was 8.

    b Find the probability that the null hypothesis would not be rejected.

She later changed her mind and decided that her alternative
hypothesis should be that the parameter was not equal to 6.
She decided to take the largest critical region for which the
probability in each 'tail' was less than 2.5%.

    c Find the critical region which she should choose.

    d Determine the exact significance level she would use
for this critical region.

21 A single observation x is to be taken from a Poisson distribution
with parameter λ.
This observation is to be used to test H_0: $\lambda = 9$ against H_1: $\lambda \neq 9$.

    a Use a 5% significance level to find the critical region for this
test.

    b State the exact significance level of this test.

The actual value of x obtained was 6.

    c State the conclusion of the test based on this value.

22 A personnel officer for a multi-national company knows from experience that 25% of the applicants she interviews in the UK are not suitable for the posts they have applied for.

She is posted to another country and wonders whether the situation will be the same there.
She has to conduct 30 interviews in the first 2 weeks.

   a Write down the null and alternative hypotheses she would use to do a hypothesis test based on these 30 interviews.

   b Find the critical region if a 5% significance level is to be used.

There were 12 applicants in the group who were not suitable.

   c State the conclusion of the test based on this information.

23 A particular model of photocopier jammed on average 4.5 times a week. A new model was brought out which claims to be less prone to jams. The office manager decides to record how many times the new model jams in the first 2 weeks to test this claim.

   a Write down the null and alternative hypotheses he would use.

   b Find the critical region if a 5% significance level is to be used.

He notes that the new model jams 3 times in the first 2 weeks.

   c Carry out the hypothesis test at the 5% significance level.

   d The firm's accountant tells the manager that he does not think it was a good idea to use the first 2 weeks of using the new model. Give a reason why he is right.

24 A large company is concerned as to whether its female employees have equal opportunities for promotion. Overall 35% of its employees are female.
The husband of the human resources manager is a statistician.
He suggests that she should take a random sample of 40 people above a certain employment grade in the company and conduct a hypothesis test of whether women are fairly represented at this level.

   a Write down the null and alternative hypotheses she would use.

   b Find the critical region if a 5% significance level is to be used.

   c When she takes the sample she finds that it contains 9 females. Carry out the hypothesis test and state your conclusion clearly.

S2

25 The number of letters received by a household follows a Poisson distribution with mean 2.5 per day.

    a What is the probability that

        i on a particular day the household receives two or more letters

        ii the total number of letters received in 2 weeks (12 days of postal deliveries) is at least 35?

        You should use a suitable approximation.

    On the Monday before Christmas, 7 letters were delivered to the household.

    b Test at the 1% level of significance whether the mean number of letters per day is higher in the week before Christmas than normally.

26 In a multiple choice examination paper, a candidate has to select which one of four possible answers to a question is correct. On a paper of 50 questions he gets 16 correct answers.

    His teacher says he can't have done any revision at all. Test, at the 10% level, whether there is evidence to suggest that he has done better than just guessing.

27 A government department was concerned at the number of laptops which had been lost. A complete audit of the previous 12 months showed that an average of 2.5 laptops per week were reported lost. New procedures were introduced in the department to try to reduce the number of laptops lost.

    In a randomly selected period of 3 weeks, some months after the introduction of the new procedures, it was found that 9 laptops were lost.

    Explain why no detailed calculations are needed to be able to say that a hypothesis test would conclude that there is no evidence to suggest that the new procedures have been effective.

28 A psychologist reads in research papers that 80% of people approved of married women working in 1988. She thinks that this has increased since then and conducts a survey of a random sample of 40 of her patients.

    a Explain why the results of her survey will not allow her to say anything about whether more people approve of women working now than in 1988.

    She takes another sample of size 40 which is appropriate.

    b **i** State the null and alternative hypotheses she would use.

        ii Find the critical region for her test.

Factorials and the binomial expansion

n factorial, $n! = n \times (n-1) \times (n-2) \times \cdots \times 3 \times 2 \times 1$

$0!$ is defined to be 1 as a special case.

Revision for Chapters 1 and 2

> The number of ways that r things can be chosen out of n is
> $$\binom{n}{r} = {}^nC_r = \frac{n!}{r!(n-r)!}$$

You can find these values by reading across the relevant row in Pascal's triangle.

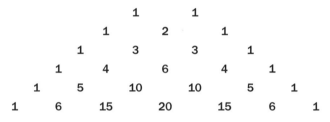

$\binom{4}{0} = 1, \binom{4}{1} = 4, \binom{4}{2} = 6$, etc

S2

> The expansion of $(a + x)^n$ is given by
> $$(a+x)^n = a^n + \binom{n}{1}a^{n-1}x + \binom{n}{2}a^{n-2}x^2 + \binom{n}{3}a^{n-3}x^3 + \cdots + x^n$$

$\binom{n}{0} = \binom{n}{n} = 1$ for any n

EXAMPLE 1

Evaluate $\binom{8}{3}$

$$\binom{8}{3} = {}^8C_3 = \frac{8!}{3! \times 5!} = \frac{8 \times 7 \times 6}{3 \times 2} = 56$$

EXAMPLE 2

Expand $(3 + x)^5$

Use the row of Pascal's triangle starting 1, 5,...:

$$(3+x)^5 = 3^5 + 5 \times 3^4 x + 10 \times 3^3 x^2 + 10 \times 3^2 x^3 + 5 \times 3x^4 + x^5$$

$$= 243 + 405x + 270x^2 + 90x^3 + 15x^4 + x^5$$

The exponential function

$$e^x = 1 + x + \frac{x^2}{2!} + \frac{x^3}{3!} + \cdots + \frac{x^n}{n!} + \cdots$$

Revision for Chapter 2

This function is used to define the probability function for the Poisson distribution.

EXAMPLE 3

Use a calculator to evaluate

a e^3 **b** $e^{0.1}$ **c** $e^{-0.5}$

a $e^3 = 20.0855\ldots$

b $e^{0.1} = 1.1051\ldots$

c $e^{-0.5} = 0.60653\ldots$

Differentiating polynomials

You can find the rate of change of a function at any point by differentiating.

Revision for Chapter 3

$$y = kx^n \Rightarrow \frac{dy}{dx} = knx^{n-1}$$

EXAMPLE 4

Differentiate $y = 5x + 3$ with respect to x.

$$y = 5x + 3 \Rightarrow \frac{dy}{dx} = 5$$

Any constant term has zero as its differential.

EXAMPLE 5

Differentiate $y = x^3 + 4x^2 - 3x + 1$ with respect to x.

$$y = x^3 + 4x^2 - 3x + 1 \Rightarrow \frac{dy}{dx} = 3x^2 + 8x - 3$$

Integrating polynomials

Revision for Chapter 3.

Integration is the inverse process to differentiation.

$$\text{Generally} \quad \int x^n \, dx = \frac{1}{n+1} x^{n+1} + c \quad \text{for all } n \neq -1$$

| Remember the constant of integration, c.

EXAMPLE 6

Evaluate $\int (x^2 + 5x - 2) \, dx$

$$\int (x^2 + 5x - 2) \, dx = \frac{1}{3}x^3 + \frac{5}{2}x^2 - 2x + c$$

Definite integration

Revision for Chapter 3.

Sometimes you have limits between which the integral is to be calculated. In this case the '$+c$' is not needed.

$$\int_a^b x^n \, dx = \left[\frac{1}{n+1} x^{n+1} \right]_a^b = \left(\frac{1}{n+1} a^{n+1} \right) - \left(\frac{1}{n+1} b^{n+1} \right)$$

S2

EXAMPLE 7

Evaluate $\int_1^3 (4x + 5) \, dx$

$$\int_1^3 (4x + 5) \, dx = \left[2x^2 + 5x \right]_1^3$$
$$= (2 \times 3^2 + 5 \times 3) - (2 \times 1^2 + 5 \times 1)$$
$$= 33 - 7 = 26$$

EXAMPLE 8

Evaluate $\int_0^1 (x^2 - 2x + 5) \, dx$

$$\int_0^4 (x^2 - 2x + 5) \, dx = \left[\frac{1}{3}x^3 - x^2 + 5x \right]_0^4$$
$$= \left(\frac{1}{3} \times 4^3 - 4^2 + 5 \times 4 \right) - 0$$
$$= \frac{64}{3} - 16 + 20 = \frac{76}{3}$$

Solving quadratic equations

You can solve quadratic equations by setting one side equal to 0 and factorising the quadratic expression on the other side, or by using the quadratic formula

$$ax^2 + bx + c = 0 \Rightarrow x = \frac{-b \pm \sqrt{b^2 - 4ac}}{2a}$$

provided $b^2 - 4ac \geqslant 0$

If $b^2 - 4ac < 0$ then the formula involves the square root of a negative number, which does not exist in the set of real numbers. In this case the quadratic will have no real solutions.

EXAMPLE 9

Solve $(2x - 1)(x + 3) = 0$

$(2x - 1)(x + 3) = 0$

$\Rightarrow x = \dfrac{1}{2}$ or $x = -3$

EXAMPLE 10

Solve $x^2 - 4x + 3 = 0$

$x^2 - 4x + 3 = 0 \Rightarrow (x - 1)(x - 3) = 0$

$\Rightarrow x = 1$ or $x = 3$

EXAMPLE 11

Solve $3x^2 + 9x + 5 = 0$

$3x^2 + 9x + 5 = 0$

$\Rightarrow x = \dfrac{-9 \pm \sqrt{9^2 - 4 \times 3 \times 5}}{2 \times 3}$

$= \dfrac{-9 \pm \sqrt{81 - 60}}{6}$

$\Rightarrow x = \dfrac{-9 \pm \sqrt{21}}{6}$

$= -2.26$ or -0.74 (to 2 d.p.)

Before you start Answers

Chapter 1
1 **a** 120   **b** 95 040
2 10.4

Exercise 1.1
1 **a** 1 7 21 35 35 21 7 1   **b** 35, 21
2 **a** 210, 1, 5005, 4950   **b** 45, 462, 1, 4.71 × 10^13
3 0.2344, 0.0938
4 0.3241, 0.0102
5 0.1419, 0.0420
6 0.0015, 0.2311
7 0.0173, 0.1366
8 0.0131, 0.0393
9 0.2344, 0.0938
10 **a** 0.0010, 0.0098, 0.0439, 0.1172
   b 0.0107, 0.9453, 0.8281
11 0.2642, 2.84 × 10^{-7}
12 0.0913, 9.09 × 10^{-13}
13 0.2373, 0.0879

Exercise 1.2
1 0.8971, 0.9991
2 0.5833, 0.0255
3 0.2855, 0.9917
4 0.5888, 0.0401
5 0.3073, 0.0003
6 0.1256

Exercise 1.3
1 **a** 17.5   **b** 8.75
2 30, 4.24
3 **a** P = 0.8, Var(X) = 4, st. dev. = 2
   b P(X > 20) = 0.4027
4 $q = 1 - p = 0.7$; $p = 0.3$; 100 trials
5 $20p(1 - p)$. Max when $p = 0.5$
6 $\mu = 0.96$, $\sigma = \sqrt{0.8448} = 0.919$, $\mu - \sigma = 0.041$, so only
   0 is $< \mu - \sigma$. Prob = 0.3596

Exercise 1.4
1 **a** No – not a fixed number of trials
   b Yes, $n = 10$, $p = \frac{1}{6}$
   c No – not constant probability (changes depending
      on the colour taken out each time)
   d Yes, $n = 5$, $p = \frac{1}{2}$
   e Yes, $n = 25$, $p = \frac{1}{6}$
   f No – not counting the number of times a
      particular outcome happens in the trials
2 **a** 0.0424, 0.1413, 0.2277, 0.2361
   b 3   **c** 3, 2.7
3 **a** **i** 0.1472   **ii** 0.1711
      iii 0.1651   **iv** 0.1337
   b 7
   c 7.5, 5.25

4 **a** Independence, probability not dependent on time
      of day (fixed number of trials (cars) is known, and
      two possible outcomes are given); $n = 40$, $p = 0.08$
   b Independence (fixed number of trials (matches) is
      known, and two possible outcomes are given,
      constant probability ok if independence is
      satisfied); $n = 48$, $p = 0.02$
   c Independence, balls indistinguishable to touch
      when withdrawing (fixed number of trials is
      known, and two possible outcomes are given);
      $n = 50$, $p = 0.3$
   d Independence (fixed number of trials is known
      and two possible outcomes (blue/not blue) are
      given); $n = 50$, $p = 0.3$
5 **a** Mean = 3, var. = 1.5
   b Mean = 2.99, var. = 3.09
   c No – while the mean is a good match, the variance
      is much greater than would be anticipated in the
      binomial.
6 **a** $p = 0.4$ or 0.6
   b 0.1285, 0.0744

Review 1
1 **a** 0.817   **b** 0.408   **c** 12.8 on average
2 **a** 0.4114   **b** 0.849, 0.0176
3 **a** 125   **b** 1.70
4 **a** 0.8245   **b** 0.1771
5 **a** 0.6826, 0.5760 **b** 0.166   **c** 2, $\sqrt{1.2} = 1.10$
   d 2.1, 1.6; mean is close to binomial, but standard
      deviation is somewhat higher – since this is a fairly
      large sample it suggests the binomial might be a
      possible first model but is not particularly good.
6 **a** 0.8392, 0.187, 0.835   **b** 210, 151.2
7 **a** 0.2186, 0.9500, 0 (7.5 is half), 0.6863
   b 9 and 1.90; 9.1 and 1.58. Mean supports claim, but
      standard deviation is smaller which suggests games
      not independent.
8 **a** 0.8392, 0.1074, 0.8308
   b B(40, 0.2) has mean 8 and variance 6.4. The mean
      is about right but his results have much more
      variance than would be expected. If the number
      of blue pegs does follow a binomial it looks as
      though he has maybe made up his results and
      ensured about the right average appears. (it is
      possible that the binomial is not a good model
      and his results are genuine).
9 **a** 16, 3.2   **b** 0.5886
10 **a** 0.8725   **b** 0.0266
11 **a** Two out of:
      i there has to be a fixed number of trials
      ii each trial must have the same two possible
         outcomes
      iii the outcomes of the trials have to be
         independent of one another
      iv the probability has to remain constant.

S2

b 0.0402, 0.314

c $(1 - 0.034)^{20} = 0.500\,659$ is the probability they do light

12 **a** 0.4114   **b** 0.210

c Independence (do the beads go onto a string randomly or does someone pick them – and ensure a balance of colours?); constant probability – that the number of beads in the set is large enough that removing some beads does not affect the probability of getting a particular colour.

Before you start Answers

Chapter 2

1 **a** 0.0498   **b** 0.1225
2   0.1008

Exercise 2.1

1 **a** 0.2707   **b** 0.1804
2 **a** 0.1607   **b** 0.2678
3 **a** 0.1239   **b** 0.1163
4 **a** 0.6703   **b** 0.2681
5 **a** 0.2692   **b** 0.1037
6 **a** 0.2087   **b** 0.3799
7 **a** 0.2087   **b** 0.6201
8 **a** 0.2303   **b** 0.6268

Exercise 2.2

1 **a** 0.2384   **b** 0.5305
2 **a** 0.2700   **b** 0.3796
3 **a** 0.1438   **b** 0.4303
4 **a** 0.1637   **b** 0.8335   **c** 0.1462

Exercise 2.3

1 **a** $P(X = 4) = \left(\dfrac{2.5}{4}\right) \times P(X = 3)$

   b 0.134   **c** Yes   **d** 2

2 **a** $P(X = 4) = \left(\dfrac{4}{4}\right) \times P(X = 3) = P(X = 3)$

   b Because up to this point probabilities are increasing, these are equal and then the probabilities start to decrease.

3 **a** $1.2 = \dfrac{\lambda}{4}$, so $\lambda = 4.8$ **b** 4

4 **a** $P(X = 7) = \dfrac{6.5}{7} \times P(X = 6)$

   b Because from part **a**, $P(X = 7) < P(X = 6)$ and up to this point $\dfrac{\lambda(= 6.5)}{x} < 1$ so $P(X = 6)$ is the largest.

5 **a** $\lambda = 9$
   b there are two modes, at 8 and 9

Exercise 2.4

1 **a** 0.7576   **b** 0.9858
2 **a** 0.2851   **b** 0.3937
3 **a** 0.1355   **b** 0.9928
4 **a** 0.8882   **b** 0.5265
5 **a** 0.6577   **b** 0.5321
6 **a** 0.1336   **b** 0.2414
7 **a** 0.1322   **b** 0.8576
8 **a** 0.2565   **b** 0.3380
9   0.2834

Exercise 2.5

1   3.2, 3.2
2   49, 7
3 **a** $3.5, \sqrt{3.5} = 1.87$
   b $P(X > 3.5) = P(X \geqslant 4) = 0.4634$
   c $P(X > 7.24) = P(X \geqslant 8) = 0.0267$
   d $P(X < -0.24) = P(X < 0) = 0$
4 **a** $6, \sqrt{6} = 2.45$
   b $P(X > 6) = 0.3937$
   c $P(X > 10.9) = P(X \geqslant 11) = 0.0426$
   d $P(X < 1.1) = P(X \leqslant 1) = 0.0174$
5   Both are small – but because the Poisson is discrete the proportion which is two standard deviations below the mean will look a bit strange – decreasing while λ increases if no more values fall below the cutoff, and then taking a jump when another value has to be included – but it will always be fairly small.

Exercise 2.6

1 **a** Yes, $\lambda = 3$
   b No – overtaking limited or not possible so independence is lost. Cars will be bunched so not random.
   c No – just before Christmas the rate is likely to be much higher than average.
   d No – the average rate is unlikely to be constant throughout the 24 hour period.
   e No – this is probably one of the busiest times, and car accidents (drink-driving common at that time) will mean there is more than one admission at a time.

2 **a** Defects occur at random, independently of one another and at a constant average rate, $\lambda = 1.6$.
   b Defects occur at random, independently of one another and at a constant average rate, $\lambda = 4$.
   c Customers arrive at random times, independently of one another and at a constant average rate, $\lambda = \dfrac{8}{3}$.

3 **a** Mean = 2.51, var. = 2.36
   b Yes, the mean and variance are almost equal.

4 **a** 0.2231, 0.1912, 0.3033, 0.1934
   b Mean rate is probably not constant throughout the day, so wouldn't use Poisson.

Exercise 2.7

1 **a** 0.1285, 0.2706, 0.2777, 0.3233
   b Using Poisson, $\lambda = 2$ gives: 0.1353, 0.2707, 0.2707, 0.3233

2 **a** If $X \sim B(n, p)$ with n large and p close to 0 then $X \sim$ *approximately* $Po(\lambda)$ with $\lambda = np$
   b 0.000125   **c** 0.1736

3   Using Poisson, with $\lambda = 10$ for number saying no, gives 0.0293

4 **a** Using exact binomial gives 0.3405
   b Using Poisson, with $\lambda = 9$, gives 0.0550

5 **a** Using Poisson, with $\lambda = 4$, gives
   i 0.0183   **ii** 0.0081
   b There is a probability of just over 11% of at least 7 supporting it in a sample of 1000 when 1 in 250 is the claimed level of support, so 7 is not a surprising result.

Review 2

1 a Po(5)   **b** 0.1755, 0.2378, 0.3328, 0.0165
c iv is much smaller because it is only one of the ways in which the event in i can happen.
2 a 0.2342, 0.0319   **b** using Po(4.5) gives 0.3423
3 a 0.7350, 0.8666, 0.2084   **b** 15
4 a 0.1736, 0.6406, 0.0111   **b** 0.0033
c Likely not to have constant average rate across all days of the week; independence compromised because a car may be hired for more than 1 day at a time
5 a 0.247   **b** 0.790   **c** 0.045
6 a B(500, 0.0015)
Independence of faulty components (occur randomly) and constant probability. They seem reasonable unless faulty components might be the result of a bad batch of some material used, in which case you are likely to get a number of faulty components occurring close together.
b Po(0.75)   **c** 0.173
7 a 0.1681   **b** 0.0839   **c** $(0.1681)^3 = 0.00475$
d Need n so that $\mathrm{Po}(X \leqslant n) \geqslant \frac{51}{52}$, so $n = 7$
8 Po(10)   **a** 0.0103   **b** 0.2565
9 a 0.273, 0.0647
b Two out of:
  i events occur at random
  ii events occur independently of one another
  iii the average rate of occurrences remains constant
  iv there is zero probability of simultaneous occurrences.
There are a variable number of working days in different months, and the weather may affect the likelihood of accidents so it may be a reasonable model but is unlikely to be an exact distribution.
10 a 0.977, 0.0198   **b** 0.0369, 0.6577
c No. Groups of variable size so total number not known.
d No – not constant average rate over this whole period
11 a 0.8088, 0.0186   **b** 0.223
c The responses from people are independent.
12 a 0.1339   **b** 0.1429
13 a 1.55   **b** 0.692, 0.331
c Distribution is Po(4.8) so $P(X = 0) = e^{-4.8} = 0.0082$

Before you start Answers

Chapter 3

1 $10x - 2$
2 $\left(\frac{1}{5}, \frac{4}{5}\right)$
3 2.54, 0.13
4 15

Exercise 3.1

1 a Continuous   **b** Discrete   **c** Continuous
d Continuous   **e** Discrete

Exercise 3.2

1 a Yes   **b** No   **c** Yes   **d** No
2 a $1, \frac{1}{2}$ **b** $\frac{1}{4}, \frac{9}{16}$
3 a 3   **b** $\frac{2}{9}$ **c** $\frac{1}{12}$ **d** 3
e $\frac{3}{2}$
4 a $\frac{1}{4}$ **b** $\frac{3}{16}$ **c** $k = \frac{2}{5}; \frac{11}{20}$ **d** $\frac{1}{8}, 0$
e $k = \frac{3}{26}, \frac{9}{16}$
5 Note: there are many ways to write the functions – you can check equivalence by removing brackets in each representation and comparing terms.

a $f(x) = \begin{cases} 0 & x < 0 \\ \frac{2}{9}(3 - x) & 0 \leqslant x \leqslant 3 \\ 0 & x > 3 \end{cases}$

b $f(x) = \begin{cases} 0 & x < 0 \\ x + \frac{1}{2} & 0 \leqslant x \leqslant 1 \\ 0 & x > 1 \end{cases}$

c $f(x) = \begin{cases} 0 & x < 0 \\ \frac{1}{4}x & 0 \leqslant x \leqslant 2 \\ \frac{1}{4}(4 - x) & 2 < x \leqslant 4 \\ 0 & x > 4 \end{cases}$

d $f(x) = \begin{cases} 0 & x < -2 \\ \frac{1}{5} & -2 \leqslant x \leqslant 2 \\ \frac{1}{10}(4 - x) & 2 < x \leqslant 4 \\ 0 & x > 4 \end{cases}$

6 a $\frac{1}{9}, \frac{11}{36}$ **b** 0.88, 1
c $\frac{1}{2}, 0.0125, 0$ **d** 0.4, 0.6

Exercise 3.3

1 a $F(x) = \begin{cases} 0 & x < 0 \\ \frac{x^2}{9} & 0 \leqslant x \leqslant 3; \frac{1}{9} \\ 1 & x > 3 \end{cases}$

b $F(x) = \begin{cases} 0 & x < 1 \\ \frac{x^2 - 1}{24} & 1 \leqslant x \leqslant 5; \frac{1}{8} \\ 1 & x > 5 \end{cases}$

c $F(x) = \begin{cases} 0 & x < 0 \\ \frac{x^2}{10} + kx & 0 \leqslant x \leqslant 2; k = \frac{3}{10}, \frac{3}{5} \\ 1 & x > 2 \end{cases}$

d $F(x) = \begin{cases} 0 & x < 0 \\ \frac{1}{27}x^3 & 0 \leqslant x \leqslant 3; \frac{1}{8} \\ 1 & x > 3 \end{cases}$

e $F(x) = \begin{cases} 0 & x < 1 \\ k(x-1) & 1 \leqslant x \leqslant 3; \\ 1 & x > 3 \end{cases} \quad k = \frac{1}{2}, \frac{3}{4}$

f $F(x) = \begin{cases} 0 & x < 1 \\ \frac{1}{6}(x^2 - 1) & 1 \leqslant x \leqslant k; \\ 1 & x > k \end{cases} \quad k = \sqrt{7}, \frac{1}{2}$

g $F(x) = \begin{cases} 0 & x < -1 \\ \frac{1}{2}k(x^2 - 1) & -1 \leqslant x \leqslant 0; \\ 1 & x > 0 \end{cases} \quad k = -2, \frac{1}{4}$

2 **a** $\frac{1}{2}$ **b** $\frac{3}{4}$ **c** 0.35

d $f(x) = \begin{cases} 0 & x < 0 \\ \frac{1}{2} & 0 \leqslant x \leqslant 2 \\ 0 & x > 2 \end{cases}$

3 **a** $\frac{1}{4}$ **b** 1   **c** 0.45

d $f(x) = \begin{cases} 0 & x < 1 \\ 2(x-1) & 1 \leqslant x \leqslant 2 \\ 0 & x > 2 \end{cases}$

4 **a** $\frac{1}{16}$ **b** $\frac{7}{16}$ **c** 0.16

d $f(x) = \begin{cases} 0 & x < 1 \\ \frac{1}{2}(x-1) & 1 \leqslant x \leqslant 3 \\ 0 & x > 3 \end{cases}$

5 **a** $\frac{1}{8}$ **b** $\frac{1}{2}$ **c** 0.855

d $f(x) = \begin{cases} 0 & x < 1 \\ x - 1 & 1 \leqslant x \leqslant 2 \\ 3 - x & 2 \leqslant x \leqslant 3 \\ 0 & x > 3 \end{cases}$

7 **a** $k = 5, f(x) = \begin{cases} 0 & x < 0 \\ \frac{1}{5} & 0 \leqslant x \leqslant 5 \\ 0 & x > 5 \end{cases}$

b $k = 4, f(x) = \begin{cases} 0 & x < 0 \\ \frac{1}{5}(2x + 4) & 0 \leqslant x \leqslant 1 \\ 0 & x > 1 \end{cases}$

c $k = 2, f(x) = \begin{cases} 0 & x < 0 \\ \frac{1}{10}(2x + 3) & 0 \leqslant x \leqslant 2 \\ 0 & x > 2 \end{cases}$

8 **a** $f(x) = \begin{cases} 0 & x < 0 \\ \frac{1}{3} & 0 \leqslant x \leqslant 3 \\ 0 & x > 3 \end{cases}$

b No, $F(1) = 1.5$ is not possible

c $f(x) = \begin{cases} 0 & x < 0 \\ \frac{1}{28}(2x + 3) & 0 \leqslant x \leqslant 4 \\ 0 & x > 4 \end{cases}$

d $f(x) = \begin{cases} 0 & x < 0 \\ \frac{2}{3}x & 0 \leqslant x \leqslant 1 \\ 1 - \frac{1}{3}x & 1 \leqslant x \leqslant 3 \\ 0 & x > 3 \end{cases}$

e No, $F(1) = \frac{1}{2}$ and 0 cannot both be true.

9 **a** $F(x) = \int_0^x \frac{1}{2}dz = \frac{1}{2}x, \quad 0 \leqslant x \leqslant 2$

b $P(Y \leqslant y) = P(X_1 \text{ and } X_2 \text{ and } X_3 \text{ are all } \leqslant y)$

$$= \left(\frac{1}{2}y\right)^3 \quad \text{for } 0 \leqslant y \leqslant 2$$

c Differentiating gives $f(y) = \frac{3}{8}y^2, \quad 0 \leqslant y \leqslant 2$;
$f(y) = 0$ otherwise

Exercise 3.4

1   4.52, 0.0830

2 **a** $\frac{2}{9}$ **b** 2, 0.5   **c** $\frac{5}{9}$, 0.186

3 $2, \frac{2}{3}$

4 **a** $\frac{4}{625}$ **b** $4, \frac{2}{3}$

    c $\frac{369}{625}, P(X > 2.367) = 0.950$

5 **a** 5   **b** $\frac{5}{6}, \frac{5}{252} = 0.0198$

    c $0.402, P(0.692 < X < 0.974) = 0.718$

6 **a** 6   **b** 12   **c** $\frac{3}{20}$

7 **a** Since he arrives at random times, the uniform distribution over the possible waiting period is sensible. 7.5, 18.75

    b $k = -\frac{2}{9}$, mean = 1, var. $= \frac{1}{2}$

8 **a** $1 = \int_{-1}^4 k(9 + 8x - x^2)dx = \left[k\left(9x + 4x^2 - \frac{x^3}{3}\right)\right]_{-1}^4$

$$= \frac{250}{3}k \Rightarrow k = \frac{3}{250}$$

    b Mean = £2125 $(E(X) = 2.125)$ St. dev. = £1218

    c $P(\text{loss}) = \int_{-1}^0 \frac{3}{250}(9 + 8x - x^2)dx$

$$= \left[\frac{3}{250}\left(9x + 4x^2 - \frac{x^3}{3}\right)\right]_{-1}^0$$

$$= \frac{3}{250} \times \frac{14}{3} = \frac{7}{125}$$

    d $P(\text{better}) = \int_{1.5}^4 \frac{3}{250}(9 + 8x - x^2)dx = 0.6875$

9 **a** $\int_0^3 ax^2(b - x)dx = 1$ and

$E(x) = \int_0^3 ax^3(b - x)dx = 1.8 \Rightarrow a = \frac{4}{27}; b = 3$

    b 0.6 mm

c It has a single peak and tails off at both ends, but has an abrupt end at 0 (reasonable) and at 3 (less reasonable). May be a reasonable first approximation, but not likely to be really good.

Exercise 3.5

1 a $\dfrac{1}{81}, \dfrac{16}{81}$ **b** $\dfrac{1}{81}x^4 = \dfrac{1}{2} \Rightarrow x = \sqrt[4]{\dfrac{81}{2}}$

c $\dfrac{1}{81}x^4 = \dfrac{1}{4} \Rightarrow x = \sqrt[4]{\dfrac{81}{4}} = \dfrac{3}{\sqrt{2}}$

2 b Two modes at 0 or 2; median = 1

3 a $1 + \dfrac{1}{\sqrt{2}}$ **b** 1.5   **c** 2

4 a $3 + \sqrt{2}$ **b** 4

5 a Median = $\sqrt{13}$, UQ = $\sqrt{19}$, mode = 5

b Median = $\sqrt[3]{\dfrac{27}{2}}$, UQ = $\sqrt[3]{\dfrac{81}{4}}$, mode = 3

c Median = $\sqrt{2}$, UQ = $\sqrt{3}$, mode = 2

d Median = $\sqrt[3]{4}$, UQ = $\sqrt[3]{6}$, mode = 2

6 F(1.36) = 0.497; F(1.37) = 0.503 so F(m) = 0.5 for m between 1.36 and 1.37

7 a $k = \dfrac{3}{392}$ **b** 5

8 b 0

c $4 - 2\sqrt{2} = 1.17$

d $\dfrac{1}{2}x - \dfrac{1}{16}x^2 = 0.3 \Rightarrow x = 0.653$

9 a $f(x) = \begin{cases} 0 & x < 2 \\ \dfrac{3}{19}x^2 & 2 \leqslant x \leqslant 3 \\ 0 & x > 3 \end{cases}$

b 3   **c** F(2.5) = 0.401; F(2.6) = 0.504

10 a $f(x) = \begin{cases} 0 & x < 0 \\ \dfrac{-1}{9}x^2 + \dfrac{4}{9}x & 0 \leqslant x \leqslant 3 \\ 0 & x > 3 \end{cases}$

b 2   **c** F(1.7) = 0.460; F(1.8) = 0.504

Review 3

1 a $\dfrac{3}{13}$ **b** 0.53   **c** $\dfrac{27}{52} = 0.519$, 0.0842

2 a $\dfrac{1}{12}$ **b** $\dfrac{1}{3}$ **c** $\dfrac{15}{8}, \dfrac{39}{64} = 0.609$

3 a $F(x) = \begin{cases} 0 & x < 0 \\ x - \dfrac{x^2}{4} & 0 \leqslant x \leqslant 2 \\ 1 & x > 2 \end{cases}$ **b** $\dfrac{1}{4}$

c $\dfrac{2}{3}, \dfrac{2}{9}$ **d** $\dfrac{5}{9}$

4 a 0.5   **b** 0.344

5 a $f(x) = \begin{cases} 0 & x < 0 \\ 6x - 6x^2 & 0 \leqslant x \leqslant 1 \\ 0 & x > 1 \end{cases}$ **b** $\dfrac{1}{2}, \dfrac{1}{20}$

6 a $\dfrac{5}{16}$

b $E(H) = \displaystyle\int_0^2 \dfrac{3}{16}(4h^2 - h^3)\,dh = \left[\dfrac{3}{16}\left(\dfrac{4}{3}h^3 - \dfrac{h^4}{4}\right)\right]_0^2 = \dfrac{5}{4}$

c $\displaystyle\int_0^2 kx^3\,dx = \left[k\dfrac{x^4}{4}\right]_0^2 = 4k = 1 \Rightarrow k = \dfrac{1}{4}$

d $\dfrac{1}{16}$ **e** 1.6 m

f 1.25 m is only just over 4 feet tall, 1.6 m is more like an average adult (female) height, so X is more likely to be true if you assume that the children guess well on average (quite a big assumption!)

7 a $\displaystyle\int_0^1 cx\,dx + \int_1^2 c(2-x)\,dx = \left[c\dfrac{x^2}{2}\right]_0^1 + \left[c\left(2x - \dfrac{x^2}{2}\right)\right]_1^2$
$= \dfrac{1}{2}c + \dfrac{1}{2}c = 1 \Rightarrow c = 1$

b $\dfrac{1}{2}$ **c** $F(y) = \begin{cases} 0 & y < 0 \\ \displaystyle\int_0^y cx\,dx & 0 \leqslant y \leqslant 1 \\ \dfrac{1}{2} + \displaystyle\int_1^y (2-x)\,dx & 1 \leqslant y \leqslant 2 \\ 1 & y > 2 \end{cases}$

gives these function forms

d 0.36

e It is reasonable, though can't be exact because there is a very large number of values.

f Sharp peak, stops abruptly at the end.

8 a 0   **b** $\displaystyle\int_0^3 \dfrac{t^2}{18}\,dt = \left[\dfrac{t^3}{54}\right]_0^3 = \dfrac{1}{2}$

c $\dfrac{4}{27}$ **d** $\dfrac{71}{24} = 2.96$ mins

9 a $f(x) = \dfrac{2}{7} - \dfrac{2}{49}x$ $0 \leqslant x \leqslant 7$ has y-intercept at $\dfrac{2}{7}$, and f(7) = 0; two points is enough to define a straight line.

b $\dfrac{9}{49}$

c $E(X) = \displaystyle\int_0^7 \left(\dfrac{2}{7}x - \dfrac{2}{49}x^2\right)dx = \left[\dfrac{1}{7}x^2 - \dfrac{2}{49} \times \dfrac{x^3}{3}\right]_0^7$
$= 7 - \dfrac{14}{3} = \dfrac{7}{3}$ mins

d $\dfrac{49}{18}$ mins²

e It has the property that she is more likely to arrive with just a short waiting time, but it is unlikely to be a straight line decrease over the full 7-minute gap between buses.

10 a 0.352   **b** 0.104

c 35 minutes (symmetry)   **d** $\dfrac{0.352}{0.896} = 0.393$

Revision exercise 1

1 0.5155

2 a 0.3585   **b** 0.0103   **c** 77

3 a 0.0352, 0.2206, 0.6850

b Mean = 300, var. = 180

4 a 0.3, 0.285   **b** $\dfrac{19}{82} = 0.232$, 0.593

c No – the mean and variance are not close to what the binomial predicts.

5 a P(0.4)   **b** 0.00793   **c** 0.1241

6 a 0.9084   **b** 9

c The same rate may not apply all the way through the year (expect some seasonal peak around Christmas for example).

7 a 0.7029, 0.1708   **b** 0.2940

c No, they are not independent – shoppers will join the shortest queue.

8 a 0.3425   **b** 0.4557

c Po(4.5) distribution; most likely is 4

9 a 0.5768   **b** £80

10 a Poisson with parameter 2 – events occur randomly in time.

b 0.215, 0.4335

11 a Two out of:

    i events occur at random

    ii events occur independently of one another

    iii the average rate of occurrences remains constant

    iv there is zero probability of simultaneous occurrences.

b 0.3773

c Mean = £34.60; variance of cost is 140.80.

12 a 0.1215; 0.1225   **b** Using Po(0.6), 0.0231

c No – there is not a fixed number of trials

13 a Two out of:

    i there has to be a fixed number of trials

    ii each trial must have the same two possible outcomes

    iii the outcomes of the trials have to be independent of one another

    iv the probability has to remain constant.

b B(20, 0.1)   **c** 0.1216, 0.0024

d 2, 1.8   **e** Po(10) 0.0487

14 a Since n is large and p is close to zero, can use Poisson with parameter 4 as an approximation to B(200, 0.02)

b 0.6288

15 a 0.512   **b** 1   **c** 0.098   **d** 1.794

e $f(x) = \begin{cases} 0 & x < 1 \\ 3(x-1)^2 & 1 \leqslant x \leqslant 2 \\ 0 & x > 2 \end{cases}$

16 b $F(x) = \begin{cases} 0 & x < 2 \\ \dfrac{x^2}{6} - \dfrac{2}{3} & 2 \leqslant x \leqslant k \\ 1 & x > k \end{cases}$ $F(k) = 1 \Rightarrow k = \sqrt{10}$

$\dfrac{5}{6}$, mean = 2.62, var. = 0.111

17 a $\dfrac{1}{50}$, $F(t) = \begin{cases} 0 & x < 0 \\ \dfrac{t^2}{100} & 0 \leqslant t \leqslant 10; \\ 1 & x > 10 \end{cases}$ 0.32

18 a $\dfrac{3}{64}$, 3, 0.6   **b** $\dfrac{37}{64}$, 0.332

19 b Symmetry   **c** 1.5

20 b $F(t) = \begin{cases} 0 & t < 5 \\ \dfrac{1}{6}t - \dfrac{t^2}{300} - \dfrac{3}{4} & 5 \leqslant t \leqslant 15 \\ 1 & t > 15 \end{cases}$

c 0.23   **d** $F(25 - 5\sqrt{10}) = 0.5$

e It starts and ends abruptly, which is unlikely to be the case.

21 a $\dfrac{1}{64}, \dfrac{27}{64}$ **b** $F(2 \times \sqrt[3]{4}) = 0.5$

c $2 \times \sqrt[3]{6} = 3.634$

22 a $\dfrac{3}{175}$ **c** 4

23 a $\dfrac{1}{9}$ **c** 3

d 2.25, 0.3375   **e** 0.160

Before you start Answers

Chapter 4

1 a 1, 2   1, 3   1, 4

    2, 1   2, 3   2, 4

    3, 1   3, 2   3, 4

    4, 1   4, 2   4, 3

b 1, 1   1, 2   1, 3   1, 4

    2, 1   2, 2   2, 3   2, 4

    3, 1   3, 2   3, 3   3, 4

    4, 1   4, 2   4, 3   4, 4

2 mean = 3.1, variance = 0.69

Exercise 4.1

1 a The population is all adults in the UK

b A sampling frame could be the government register of national insurance numbers (voting registers will miss a lot of eligible people who have not registered to vote/ who are in prison etc.). There will be people on the list who are currently abroad, visitors and immigrants who do not have a NI number.

2 Every member of the population has an equal chance of being selected at any stage, and all possible combinations are equally likely.

3 a The customers of the bank.

b Combine alphabetical lists of holders of all different types of account the bank offers.

c Some individuals will have more than one account, sometimes in more than one name, e.g. married women may still have an account in their maiden name, some people have a different professional name in which they also hold accounts.

4 The first named person is more likely to be male.

Exercise 4.2

2 Any context in which the easy availability is a major factor – so asking friends or going to one site and asking passers-by would be examples.

3 a A census would mean all the batteries had been tested and this would be very expensive.

b If there was a problem with a batch of components you might find a group of defectives appearing together. The main advantage is that it is very easy to do what is suggested. An alternative would be to take a random sample of batteries earlier in the packing stages until you have 50.

4 a A bank will have a very large number of customers.

b They might want to make sure their 'high value' customers are over-represented in any sample that they take, to make sure they address any concerns they have.

Exercise 4.3

1 **a** Yes **b** Yes **c** Yes **d** Yes
   e No – it has μ, σ in it and not just the values from the observations.

2 **a** $B\left(20, \frac{1}{3}\right)$ **b** 0.0143 **c** $\frac{20}{3}, \frac{40}{9}$

3 **a** B(10, 0.75) **b** 0.4744 **c** 7.5, 1.875

4 **a** 2.6 **b** 111, 113, 131, 133, 311, 313, 331, 333
   c These 8 possibilities are not equally likely; they have probabilities 0.008, 0.032, 0.032, 0.128, 0.032, 0.128, 0.128, 0.512 So the sampling distribution is:

Value of mean	1	$\frac{5}{3}$	$\frac{7}{3}$	3
Probability	0.008	0.096	0.384	0.512

   d The mode is either 1 (when at least two 1s appear) or 3 (when at least two 3s appear)

Value of mode	1	3
Probability	0.104	0.896

   e The median will always be the same as the mode (there are only two possible values on each of three observations).

Value of median	1	3
Probability	0.104	0.896

5 **a** 3.8
   b

Sample	11	13	16	31	33	36	61	63	66
Probability	0.04	0.08	0.08	0.08	0.16	0.16	0.08	0.16	0.16

   c

Sample mean	1	2	3	3.5	4.5	6
Probability	0.04	0.16	0.16	0.16	0.32	0.16

   d With only two observations the median and the mean will be the same in each case:

Sample median	1	2	3	3.5	4.5	6
Probability	0.04	0.16	0.16	0.16	0.32	0.16

Review 4

1 **a** Some pupils might travel a lot on the weekend or party too hard and absentee rates might be higher than on other days.
   b Take a stratified sample using a number of each school day.

2 **a** A population is the full group which is of interest, and a sampling frame is a list of all the members of the population.
   b The vehicle licensing authority has a register of car owners with details of their car, including whether it is diesel powered. A list compiled from hospital and GP records in the Oxford area.

However, it is unlikely in both cases that a market research company will be able to access such records legitimately.

3 **a** The catalogue of books in the library
   b The individual books
   c She could assign a number to each book in the catalogue and use random numbers to take the sample.
   d Since these books were being returned they are likely to over-represent popular books and this is likely to be an over-estimate i.e. the true mean is likely to be lower than 8.2.

4 **a** The club membership list – which might be alphabetical or by date of joining.
   b A census would seek the views of all members of the club while a sample will use a subset of the membership.
   c A census takes more time/effort/expense

5 **a** Advantage – cheaper/quicker/easier; disadvantage is that the census would give you complete knowledge whereas the sample gives you partial information. In this case a census means doing it over a long period so all books are examined when they are returned, but with a sample you would not know if some books have been lost or damaged beyond repair and are not being returned as a result.
   b The catalogue of books in the library
   c The individual books
   d No – the books on the top shelves are not as accessible and therefore less likely to be damaged so this method is biased (likely to under-estimate the amount of damage). Also, childrens' books are more likely to be damaged than adults' books (so they tend to over-estimate).

6 **a** This is a convenience sample – it only takes people in one place in the centre of Manchester, and it takes women (not necessarily even housewives) who are there at 9 on a Monday so it includes people not in the required population and excludes others who are in the population of interest.
   b Not all numbers are equally likely – indeed 1–5 cannot possibly be taken. Not all the suppliers will be listed in the Yellow Pages.
   c The telephone directory is not the same as the list of voters – some people are ex-directory; many people now only have mobile phones; only one adult at a residence will be listed (so women will be under-represented with this method). The pages of the book are not equally likely to occur when the book is dropped (if the book is used regularly, then it may open at one of the pages commonly used, otherwise it is more likely to open at a page near the middle).

7 **a** A population is the full group which is of interest, and a sampling frame is a list of all the members of the population.
   b If the population is the membership of a club and the membership list is used as a sampling frame the two may not be the same if the membership list is not kept up to date.

c A census can be used when the population is relatively small and accessible or if the question is very important, where a sample will be used when the population is large and a census is going to be too expensive/difficult.

Before you start Answers

Chapter 5

1 mean = 2.4, variance = 1.68
2 mean = 7.3, variance = 7.3
3 **a** 0.9772   **b** 0.3707   **c** 0.3596

Exercise 5.1

1 **a** $4, \frac{16}{3}$ **b** $13.5, \frac{3}{4}$ **c** $0, \frac{100}{12} = \frac{25}{3}$

2 **a** $2, \frac{4}{3}$ **b** $7, \frac{4}{3}$ **c** $-6, \frac{4}{3}$ **d** $3, \frac{25}{3}$

3 **a** 2   **b** 3   **c** $\frac{1}{6}$

4 **a** $\text{Var}(x) = \frac{1}{3}$ means $b - a$ (max − min) = 2, and symmetry of mean tells you $a = 6$, $b = 8$.

$$f(x) = \begin{cases} 0 & x < 6 \\ \frac{1}{2} & 6 \leqslant x \leqslant 8 \\ 0 & x > 8 \end{cases}$$

b $F(x) = \begin{cases} 0 & x < 6 \\ \frac{1}{2}(x - 6) & 6 \leqslant x \leqslant 8 \\ 1 & x > 8 \end{cases}$

5 0.887

6 **a** $f(x) = \begin{cases} 10 & -0.05 \leqslant x \leqslant 0.05 \\ 0 & \text{otherwise} \end{cases}$

b $\frac{1}{1200}$ **c** −0.025

7 30 cm, 300 cm²

8 **a** $\frac{24.5}{40} = 0.6125$

b Because it is smaller it has more chance of ending up completely between the lines

c At 18 mm, there is a < 50% chance of losing your coin so the operator does not want to play …

Exercise 5.2

1 **a** $P(Y < 41.5)$ **b** $P(Y > 31.5)$
   c $P(Y > 8.5)$ **d** $P(42.5 < Y < 84.5)$
2 **a** Yes, N(35, 10.5)
   b No, $n(1 - p) = 10 \times 0.3 = 3 < 5$ (with only 10, there should be no problem in using the exact binomial instead of looking at an approximation)
   c Yes, N(100, 80)
   d No, $np = 500 \times 0.002 = 1$ (the Poisson would be appropriate here)
3 **a** 0.978   **b** 0.886   **c** 0.511
   d 0.827   **e** 0.629
4 **a** 0.6923; 0.6973   **b** 0.005; 0.72%
5 If $X \sim B(n, p)$ and if n is large and p is close to 0.5, so that the distribution is nearly symmetrical, then the normal distribution can be used to approximate the binomial. One generally accepted rule of thumb is that the normal can be used as an approximation when both np and $n(1 - p)$ are > 5. The parameters to be used are the mean and variance of the binomial, i.e. $\mu = np$; $\sigma^2 = npq$ in $N(\mu, \sigma^2)$
6 **a** 0.2342   **b** 0.9344   **c** 0.0268
7 **a** $B\left(50, \frac{1}{4}\right)$ **b** 0.0139   **c** 0.8023
8 **a** 0.869
   b People attending the surgery are likely to have a higher proportion with health problems than in the register as a whole, so it is not a reasonable assumption, particularly in the context of looking for a particular ailment.

Exercise 5.3

1 **a** $P(Y < 15.5)$ **b** $P(Y > 22.5)$
   c $P(Y < 17.5)$ **d** $P(44.5 < Y < 61.5)$
2 **a** Yes, N(16, 16)   **b** Yes, N(12.32, 12.32)
   c No since $\lambda < 10$
3 **a** 0.142   **b** 0.861   **c** 0.916
   d 0.163   **e** 0.611
4 **a** 0.6443, 0.6512   **b** 0.007, 1.1%
5 For large λ (>10) you can use a normal approximation with parameters equal to the mean and variance of the Poisson, i.e. $\mu = \sigma^2 = \lambda$.
6 **a** 0.1850   **b** 0.123
7 **a** 0.2510   **b** 0.614
8 0.8186
9 **a** 0.1318   **b** 0.948   **c** 0.953
10 **a** 0.0858   **b** 0.659
   c i Assumed 7 days mail delivered on the Monday (i.e Mon–Sat and Mon) Assumed that average rate of arrival of mail is constant throughout 6-day week.
   ii There could be a peak on Mondays as customers write to the office over the weekend, so not all that reasonable.

Review 5

1 **a** 0.0159   **b** N(12.5, 11.875), 0.527
2 **a** 13   **b** $10.5, \frac{25}{12}$ **c** 0.211
3 **a** 0.8095, 0.1235
   b N(37, 37) 0.143, high likelihood that demand will be greater than the number of rooms available.
4 **a** 0.6768, 0.1429, 6   **b** N(68, 68), 0.0648
   c Yes; No – not independent since calls getting engaged tone will try again; No – not constant average rate throughout the year.
5 **a** 0.8497, 0.3504   **b** N(132.5, 62.275), 0.951
   c 0.425
6 **a** 0.159, 0.0464   **b** N(54.6, 38.22), 0.442
   c If there are factors which will affect all people at the same time (for example the weather might make a difference) then independence will not be plausible but otherwise it should be reasonable. Independence also assumes they are all given the same treatment.
7 **a** B(20, 0.05)   **b** 0.1887, 0.0026
   c $P(7.5) - 0.0746$ N(7.5, 7.125) 0.0656
   d The normal is a continuous distribution being used to approximate a discrete distribution
   e Both are reasonably good – around 6.5 to 7.5%.

8 a 0.815, 0.168, 0.353 **b** Po(9), 0.197

9 a Two out of:
   i events occur at random
   ii events occur independently of one another
   iii the average rate of occurrences remains constant
   iv there is zero probability of simultaneous occurrences.
 b 0.133 **c** 11
 d $N(20, 20)$ 0.712

10 a 0.805 **b** $N(67.7, 44.8)$; 0.028
 c Po(4.5) 0.658

Before you start Answers

Chapter 6

1 6 2 4

Exercise 6.1

1 $B(40, p)$; H_0: $p = 0.23$ vs H_1: $p > 0.23$

2 Do not reject H_0. Conclude there is not sufficient evidence to suggest that the proportion of applications from people with A-level Maths has increased at the 5% significance level.

3 **a** H_0: $\lambda = 4.5$ vs H_1: $\lambda \neq 4.5$
 b Reject H_0 and conclude there is sufficient evidence to suggest that the mean number of accidents is different at the weekend at the 5% significance level.

4 There is sufficient evidence at the 5% level of significance to suggest that the proportion of applications from people with A-level mathematics has increased from 23%.

5 There is not sufficient evidence at the 5% level of significance to suggest that the number of accidents is different at weekends than on weekdays.

Exercise 6.2

1 **a** 2-tailed, $X \leqslant 5$ or $X \geqslant 15$; 4.14%
 b 1-tailed, $X \leqslant 6$; 5.77%
 c 2-tailed, $X \leqslant 4$ or $X \geqslant 16$; 1.18%

2 2-tailed, $X \leqslant 8$ or $X \geqslant 22$; 4.34%

3 2-tailed, $X \leqslant 26$ or $X \geqslant 37$; 4.79%

4 2-tailed, $X \leqslant 2$ or $X \geqslant 15$; 3.11%

5 1-tailed, $X \geqslant 15$; 6%

6 1-tailed, $X \leqslant 2$; 0.93%

7 1-tailed, $X \geqslant 10$; 8.4%

Exercise 6.3

1 $X \sim B(50, p)$, H_0: $p = 0.4$ vs H_1: $p > 0.4$
 The critical region for the standard 5% test is $X \geqslant 27$, so reject the null hypothesis and conclude there is evidence at the 5% level of significance to suggest that the proportion of people who would vote for the President is greater than 40%. The actual level of significance is 3.1%.

2 $X \sim B(40, p)$, H_0: $p = 0.2$ vs H_1: $p > 0.2$
 The critical region for the standard 5% test is $X \geqslant 13$ (with an actual level of significance of 4.3%), so reject

the null hypothesis and conclude there is evidence at the 5% level of significance to suggest that she has done better than by just guessing.

3 **a** $X \sim B(25, p)$, H_0: $p = 0.2$ vs H_1: $p \neq 0.2$
 $P(X \leqslant 1) = 2.74\%$ and $P(X \geqslant 11) = 1.73\%$
 so the critical region is $X \leqslant 1$ or $X \geqslant 11$
 (i.e. 0, 1, 11, 12, … 25)
 b The exact significance level is 4.5%.

4 $X \sim B(50, p)$, H_0: $p = 0.05$ vs H_1: $p > 0.05$
 The critical region for the standard 5% test is $X \geqslant 7$ (with an actual level of significance of 3.8%), so do not reject the null hypothesis and conclude there is not sufficient evidence at the 5% level of significance to suggest that the error rate is higher than normal during a thunderstorm.

Exercise 6.4

1 **a** H_0: $\lambda = 9.5$ vs H_1: $\lambda \neq 9.5$.
 5% critical region is $X \leqslant 3$ or $X \geqslant 16$, 3.26%
 b Do not reject H_0. Conclude there is not sufficient evidence at the 5% level to suggest that the mean is not 9.5.

2 **a** Poisson (3) **b** 0.8009
 c P(< 5 in one month) = 0.8153; P(< 5 in all 12 months) = $0.8153^{12} = 0.0863$ so the probability that the crossing is installed is 0.9137.
 d Need 0 accidents in 1 month to suggest improvement; need no more than 4 accidents in 3 months to suggest improvement.
 e i Shorter
   ii Better in determining whether there has really been an improvement (not so influenced by a single event).

3 **a** Poisson, because events occur randomly in time.
 b Po(20) can be approximated by $N(20, 20)$, 0.0096
 c Unless it is an international website it is likely that the rate during the middle of the night will be different.
 d For $\frac{1}{2}$ hour, test is H_0: $\lambda = 10$ vs H_1: $\lambda \neq 10$
  5% critical region is $X \leqslant 3$ or $X \geqslant 17$.
  Insufficient evidence to reject H_0. [$X = 4$ would have been significant at the 6% level since $P(X \leqslant 4) = 2.93\%$]

Review 6

1 **a** 0.8088 $N(18, 18)$; 0.278
 b H_0: $\lambda = 9$ vs H_1: $\lambda > 9$.
  5% critical region is $X \geqslant 15$.
  Reject H_0 and conclude there is evidence to suggest that the arrival rate is higher than in the morning.

2 **a** Poisson
 b H_0: $\lambda = 2$ vs H_1: $\lambda > 2$.
  5% critical region is $X \geqslant 5$.
  Reject H_0 and conclude there is evidence to suggest that the mean number of flaws is higher than 2 per length.
 c Reducing the significance level from 5% to 1% reduces the possibility of one sort of error but in

S2

doing so automatically increases the risk of another so he needs to be clear what sort of error he is most concerned about.

3 H_0: $\lambda = 4.2$ vs H_1: $\lambda < 4.2$
10% critical region is $X \leqslant 1$.
Reject H_0 and conclude there is evidence to suggest that the process has reduced the rate of occurrence of flaws.

4 B(50, p); H_0: $p = 0.25$ vs H_1: $p > 0.25$
5% critical region is $X \geqslant 18$.
Reject H_0 and conclude there is evidence to suggest that she has done better than just guessing.

5 a H_0: $\lambda = 7$ vs H_1: $\lambda \neq 7$.
5% critical region is $X \leqslant 2$ or $X \geqslant 13$.
   b 4.56%
   c Do not reject H_0. Conclude there is not sufficient evidence to suggest that the mean is not 7.

6 H_0: $\lambda = 2.4$ against H_1: $\lambda < 2.4$
The critical region at the 10% level of significance is only the case with 0 flaws (actual level of significance is 9.1%), so do not reject H_0. Conclude that there is not sufficient evidence to suggest the mean rate has decreased from 0.3 flaws per m^2.

7 a $X \sim$ B(30, p), H_0: $p = 0.35$ vs H_1: $p > 035$
The critical region for the standard 5% test is $X \geqslant 16$ (actual level of significance is 3.0%), so reject the null hypothesis and conclude there is evidence at the 5% level of significance to suggest that the procedure has been effective.
   b To test whether people use a new procedure immediately after it is introduced and is fresh in their minds is no guarantee that in the longer term it will be effective in changing behaviour. A better test would be to collect a random sample from one or more weekends some time after the procedure has been introduced.

8 $X \sim$ B(50, p), H_0: $p = 0.25$ vs H_1: $p > 0.25$
The critical region for the standard 5% test is $X \geqslant 18$, so the null hypothesis cannot be rejected. Conclude there is not sufficient evidence at the 5% level of significance to suggest that he has done better than just guessing.

9 a The critical region for the standard 5% test is $X \leqslant 3$
   b 1.5%
   c 5 does not lie in the critical region so the null hypothesis cannot be rejected. Conclude there is not sufficient evidence at the 5% level of significance to suggest that the mean is less than 9.

10 a Po(3.5)   b 0.0302   c 0.1424
   d Sheep no longer randomly spaced
   e H_0: $\lambda = 3.5$ against H_1: $\lambda > 3.5$, so the critical region at the 1% level of significance is $X \geqslant 9$. Do not reject H_0 and conclude that there is not sufficient evidence to suggest the mean number of sheep in a square in this field is higher.

Revision exercise 2

1 a U(−0.5, 0.5)   b 0.4   c 0.16

2 a 2, 2
   b 11, 12, 15, 21, 22, 25, 51, 52, 55 with probabilities
$\frac{1}{4}, \frac{1}{6}, \frac{1}{12}, \frac{1}{6}, \frac{1}{9}, \frac{1}{18}, \frac{1}{12}, \frac{1}{18}, \frac{1}{36}$

   c

Mean	1	1.5	2	3	3.5	5
Probability	$\frac{1}{4}$	$\frac{1}{3}$	$\frac{1}{9}$	$\frac{1}{6}$	$\frac{1}{9}$	$\frac{1}{36}$

3 a Large membership. Therefore will be expensive and time consuming to do a census.
   b Alphabetical list of all the members
   c Each individual member of the club

4 a A function only of the observations
   b The sample mean $\bar{x} = \dfrac{\sum\limits_{i=1}^{n} x_i}{n}$ (or any function of just the x-values)
   c A list of the possible values of Y with corresponding probabilities

5 a Quicker, easier, cheaper
   b The membership list of the club
   c The individual club members

6 Qualitative **b**, **c** & **e**; quantitative **a**, **d** & **f**

7 a Continuous   b Discrete
   c Continuous   d Continuous

8 a Poisson, 0.185, 0.3007   b B(6, 0.45) 0.278
   c B(400, 0.14) − use N(56, 48.16) to approximate; 0.174

9 a 0.2424
   b Po(52.5), approximate by N(52.5, 52.5), 0.135, 69

10 a 0.206   b 0.109   c 0

11 a 0.223, 0.261   b 0.257
   c Use N(22.5, 12.375)   0.197

12 a U(180, 200)   i.e $f(x) = \begin{cases} 0 & x < 180 \\ 0.05 & 180 \leqslant x \leqslant 200 \\ 0 & x > 200 \end{cases}$
   b $\frac{3}{20}$, 0   c 10   d 186.67
   e One third of the way through the interval from 180 to 200

13 a 0.175   b $\frac{1}{4}$ c 0.9861

14 a 0.0718   b 0.098
   c B(250, 0.1), approximate by N(25, 22.5); 0.001

15 a 1.5, $\frac{25}{12}$ b 0.423

16 a 7−12$\sqrt{3}$ b 0.548

17 a 0.1702, 0.2293   b 0.393
   c Use Po(0.2) to approximate; 0.819
   d N(45.6, 38.67), 0.215

18 a $\frac{1}{4}$ b 0.7759
   c N(25, 18.75), 0.898

19 **a** 0.209, 0.380

   b Po(22.4), approximate by N(22.4, 22.4); 0.256

   c Not independent – likely that mothers/doctors will delay births if possible and induce others a little early.

20 **a** 8.4%   **b** 0.7166

   c $X \leqslant 1$ (1.74%) and $X \geqslant 12$ (2.01%)   **d** 3.75%

21 **a** $X \leqslant 3$ (2.12%) and $X \geqslant 16$ (2.2%)   **b** 4.32%

   c (Do not reject H_0) and conclude there is not sufficient evidence to suggest that the mean is not 9 at the 5% significance level.

22 **a** B(30, p); H_0: $p = 0.25$ vs H_1: $p \neq 0.25$.

   b 5% critical region is $X \leqslant 3$ (3.74%) and $X \geqslant 13$ (2.16%).

   c (Do not reject H_0) and conclude there is not sufficient evidence to suggest that the proportion is not 0.25 at the 5% significance level.

23 **a** H_0: $\lambda = 9$ vs H_1: $\lambda < 9$

   b 5% critical region is $X \leqslant 4$.

   c Reject H_0 and conclude there is evidence to suggest that the mean number of jams is less with the new model.

   d Machine is just new so it may be less likely to jam, or staff not being used to it may be more likely to cause jams.

24 **a** B(40, p); H_0: $p = 0.35$ vs H_1: $p < 0.35$

   b 5% critical region is $X \leqslant 8$

   c Reject H_0 and conclude there is evidence to suggest that females are under-represented at senior level.

25 **a** 0.7127, Po(30) so use N(30, 30) to approximate 0.206.

   b H_0: $\lambda = 2.5$ vs H_1: $\lambda > 2.5$

   1% critical region is $X \geqslant 7$. Reject H_0 and conclude there is evidence to suggest that the mean number of letters per day is higher in the week before Christmas.

26 B(50, p); H_0: $p = 0.25$ vs H_1: $p > 0.25$

   10% critical region is $X \geqslant 17$

   (Do not reject H_0) and conclude there is not sufficient evidence to suggest that he has done better than guessing.

27 The mean per week is 3 in this period compared with previous mean of only 2.5 so it cannot provide evidence of an improvement.

28 **a** The sample is only of her patients, who by definition are not representative of the whole population.

   b B(40, p); H_0: $p = 0.8$ vs H_1: $p > 0.8$

   5% critical region is $X \geqslant 37$ (2.85% is actual significance level)

Bias Bias occurs in a sampling method where there is tendency for a sample selected to over- or under-represent certain groups

Binomial distribution X follows a Binomial distribution if

$$P(X = r) = \binom{n}{r} p^r q^{n-r} \text{ for } r = 0, 1, 2 \dots n.$$

Census A census gathers information on every member of the population.

Continuity correction If X is a discrete distribution which is to be approximated by a continuous distribution Y then

$$P(X = x) \overset{approx}{\approx} P(x - 0.5 < Y < x + 0.5).$$

Continuous uniform (rectangular) distribution If a continuous random variable, X, has a uniform distribution over the interval (α, β), then it will have probability density function given

by $f(x) = \begin{cases} \dfrac{1}{\beta - \alpha} & \alpha \leqslant x \leqslant \beta, \\ 0 & \text{otherwise.} \end{cases}$

Critical region and critical values. The critical region for a test is the set of values for which the null hypothesis will be rejected. The critical value(s) are the boundary values of the critical region i.e. the first value at either end for which H_0 would be rejected.

Cumulative distribution function

$F(x_0) = P(X \leqslant x_0) = \displaystyle\int_{-\infty}^{x_0} f(x)dx$ is the cumulative distribution function for the random variable X and $f(x) = \dfrac{d}{dx}(F(x))$.

Data logging Any process where data are collected by some automated process, often electronic.

Mean and variance of a Binomial distribution
If $X \sim B(n, p)$, then $E(X) = np$; $Var(X) = (\sigma^2) = npq = np(1-p)$.

Mean and variance of a Poisson distribution If $X \sim \lambda$ (l), then $E(X) = \lambda$; $Var(X) = \lambda \Rightarrow$ st. dev $(\sigma) = \sqrt{\lambda}$.

Mean or expectation and variance of a continuous random variable The mean or expected value of a continuous random variable is defined as $\mu = E(X) = \displaystyle\int_{-\infty}^{\infty} x, f(x)dx$

$Var(X)$ is $E[\{X - \mu\}^2] = E(X^2) - \mu^2$.

Mean, median and variance of a continuous uniform distribution If a continuous random variable, X, has a uniform distribution over the interval (a, b) then

median = mean = $E(X) = \dfrac{\alpha + \beta}{2}$, and $Var(X) = \dfrac{(\beta - \alpha)^2}{12}$

Median of a continuous distribution If $F(x)$ is the cumulative distribution function and m is the median then $F(m) = 0.5$

Mode of a continuous distribution The mode of a continuous random variable is the value of x for which $f(x)$ is a maximum over the interval in which $f(x)$ exists. This is either a stationary point, at which $f'(x) = 0$ or one of the ends of the interval over which $f(x)$ is defined.

Natural variation There is natural variation between individual sampling units, which is due to chance, but there are often systematic differences between groups of sampling units with one or more shared characteristics, for example there are often differences between males and females.

Normal approximation to the Binomial distribution If $X \sim B(n, p)$ and n is large and p is close to 0.5, then the Normal (np, npq) can be used to approximate the distribution.

Normal approximation to the Poisson distribution If $X \sim P(\lambda)$ and λ is large (>10) then the Normal (λ, λ) can be used to approximate the distribution.

Null and alternative hypotheses The null hypothesis provides the probability basis under which the test is to be considered – the observed value of the statistic is compared with the sampling distribution if the null hypothesis was true. The alternative hypothesis is what you will turn to if the observed value is a rare event when the null hypothesis is true.

Parameters A parameter for a probability distribution is some quantity whose value is needed to know the explicit form of the distribution, for example the number of trials and the probability of success on any trial for the Binomial.

Poisson distribution X follows a Poisson distribution if

$$P(X = r) = \dfrac{e^{-\lambda} \lambda^r}{r!} \text{ for } r = 0, 1, 2 \dots$$

Poisson distribution as an approximation to the Binomial If $X \sim B(n, p)$ with n large and p close to 0 then $X \sim$ approximately $P(l)$ with $l = np$

Population The entire group of people or things which is of interest, from which samples are drawn or on which a census will be conducted.

Probability density function $f(x)$ is the probability density function (pdf) for X if $P(a < x < b) = \displaystyle\int_{b}^{a} f(x)dx$ for all values of a, b and certain conditions are satisfied.

Quartiles of a continuous distribution If F(x) is the cumulative distribution function and Q_1 and Q_3 are the lower and upper quartiles then F(Q_1) = 0.25 and F(Q_3) = 0.75

Random variables (continuous) A random variable is a quantity that can take any value determined by the outcome of a random event. A continuous random variable is one where the outcomes lie in an interval.

Recurrence relation If X ~ P(l) then the recurrence relation $P(X = k + 1) = \frac{\lambda}{k+1} \times P(X = k)$ allows you to calculate the probability of the next value in a Poisson distribution.

Sample A sample is a subset of the population.

Sampling distribution of a statistic The probability distribution of values a statistic can take is known as the sampling distribution of the statistic.

Sampling frame A sampling frame is a list containing all the units or elements which are the members of the population to be sampled.

Significance level or size of a test
Significance level = size of a hypothesis test = probability of rejecting the null hypothesis when it was actually true.

Simple random sampling Simple random sampling means sampling without replacement where each member of the population has an equal chance of being selected, and all possible combinations are equally likely.

Standard deviation of a random variable A measure of spread of the distribution. It is the square root of the variance.

Statistic A statistic is a function only of the observed data values – it can not require knowledge of any parameter values.

S2

Formulae

The following formulae and tables will be given to you in the exam formulae booklet.
You may also require those formulae listed under Statistics S1, and also those listed under
Core Mathematics C1 and C2.

Discrete distributions

Standard discrete distributions:

Distribution of X	$P(X = x)$	Mean	Variance
Binomial B(n, p)	$\binom{n}{x} p^x (1-p)^{n-x}$	np	$np(1-p)$
Poisson Po(λ)	$e^{-\lambda} \dfrac{\lambda^x}{x!}$	λ	λ

Continuous distributions

For a continuous random variable X having probability density function f

Expectation (mean): $E(X) = \mu = \displaystyle\int x f(x)\, dx$

Variance: $\text{Var}(X) = \sigma^2 = \displaystyle\int (x - \mu)^2 f(x)\, dx = \int x^2 f(x)\, dx - \mu^2$

For a function g(X): $E(g(X)) = \displaystyle\int g(x) f(x)\, dx$

Cumulative distribution function: $F(x_0) = P(X \leqslant x_0) = \displaystyle\int_{-\infty}^{x_0} f(t)\, dt$

Standard continuous distribution:

Distribution of X	P.D.F.	Mean	Variance
Uniform (Rectangular) on $[a,b]$	$\dfrac{1}{b-a}$	$\dfrac{1}{2}(a+b)$	$\dfrac{1}{12}(b-a)^2$

BINOMIAL CUMULATIVE DISTRIBUTION FUNCTION

The tabulated value is $P(X \leqslant x)$, where X has a binomial distribution with index n and parameter p.

$p =$	0.05	0.10	0.15	0.20	0.25	0.30	0.35	0.40	0.45	0.50
$n = 5, x = 0$	0.7738	0.5905	0.4437	0.3277	0.2373	0.1681	0.1160	0.0778	0.0503	0.0312
1	0.9774	0.9185	0.8352	0.7373	0.6328	0.5382	0.4284	0.3370	0.2562	0.1875
2	0.9988	0.9914	0.9734	0.9421	0.8965	0.8369	0.7648	0.6826	0.5931	0.5000
3	1.0000	0.9995	0.9978	0.9933	0.9844	0.9692	0.9460	0.9130	0.8688	0.8125
4	1.0000	1.0000	0.9999	0.9997	0.9990	0.9976	0.9947	0.9898	0.9815	0.9688
$n = 6, x = 0$	0.7351	0.5314	0.3771	0.2621	0.1780	0.1176	0.0754	0.0467	0.0277	0.0156
1	0.9672	0.8857	0.7765	0.6554	0.5339	0.4202	0.3191	0.2333	0.1636	0.1094
2	0.9978	0.9842	0.9527	0.9011	0.8306	0.7443	0.6471	0.5443	0.4415	0.3438
3	0.9999	0.9987	0.9941	0.9830	0.9624	0.9295	0.8826	0.8208	0.7447	0.6563
4	1.0000	0.9999	0.9996	0.9984	0.9954	0.9891	0.9777	0.9590	0.9308	0.8906
5	1.0000	1.0000	1.0000	0.9999	0.9998	0.9993	0.9982	0.9959	0.9917	0.9844
$n = 7, x = 0$	0.6983	0.4783	0.3206	0.2097	0.1335	0.0824	0.0490	0.0280	0.0152	0.0078
1	0.9556	0.8503	0.7166	0.5767	0.4449	0.3294	0.2338	0.1586	0.1024	0.0625
2	0.9962	0.9743	0.9262	0.8520	0.7564	0.6471	0.5323	0.4199	0.3164	0.2266
3	0.9998	0.9973	0.9879	0.9667	0.9294	0.8740	0.8002	0.7102	0.6083	0.5000
4	1.0000	0.9998	0.9988	0.9953	0.9871	0.9712	0.9444	0.9037	0.8471	0.7734
5	1.0000	1.0000	0.9999	0.9996	0.9987	0.9962	0.9910	0.9812	0.9643	0.9375
6	1.0000	1.0000	1.0000	1.0000	0.9999	0.9998	0.9994	0.9984	0.9963	0.9922
$n = 8, x = 0$	0.6634	0.4305	0.2725	0.1678	0.1001	0.0576	0.0319	0.0168	0.0084	0.0039
1	0.9428	0.8131	0.6572	0.5033	0.3671	0.2553	0.1691	0.1064	0.0632	0.0352
2	0.9942	0.9619	0.8948	0.7969	0.6785	0.5518	0.4278	0.3154	0.2201	0.1445
3	0.9996	0.9950	0.9786	0.9437	0.8862	0.8059	0.7064	0.5941	0.4770	0.3633
4	1.0000	0.9996	0.9971	0.9896	0.9727	0.9420	0.8939	0.8263	0.7396	0.6367
5	1.0000	1.0000	0.9998	0.9988	0.9958	0.9887	0.9747	0.9502	0.9115	0.8555
6	1.0000	1.0000	1.0000	0.9999	0.9996	0.9987	0.9964	0.9915	0.9819	0.9648
7	1.0000	1.0000	1.0000	1.0000	1.0000	0.9999	0.9998	0.9993	0.9983	0.9961
$n = 9, x = 0$	0.6302	0.3874	0.2316	0.1342	0.0751	0.0404	0.0207	0.0101	0.0046	0.0020
1	0.9288	0.7748	0.5995	0.4362	0.3003	0.1960	0.1211	0.0705	0.0385	0.0195
2	0.9916	0.9470	0.8591	0.7382	0.6007	0.4628	0.3373	0.2318	0.1495	0.0898
3	0.9994	0.9917	0.9661	0.9144	0.8343	0.7297	0.6089	0.4826	0.3614	0.2539
4	1.0000	0.9991	0.9944	0.9804	0.9511	0.9012	0.8283	0.7334	0.6214	0.5000
5	1.0000	0.9999	0.9994	0.9969	0.9900	0.9747	0.9464	0.9006	0.8342	0.7461
6	1.0000	1.0000	1.0000	0.9997	0.9987	0.9957	0.9888	0.9750	0.9502	0.9102
7	1.0000	1.0000	1.0000	1.0000	0.9999	0.9996	0.9986	0.9962	0.9909	0.9805
8	1.0000	1.0000	1.0000	1.0000	1.0000	1.0000	0.9999	0.9997	0.9992	0.9980
$n = 10, x = 0$	0.5987	0.3487	0.1969	0.1074	0.0563	0.0282	0.0135	0.0060	0.0025	0.0010
1	0.9139	0.7361	0.5443	0.3758	0.2440	0.1493	0.0860	0.0464	0.0233	0.0107
2	0.9885	0.9298	0.8202	0.6778	0.5256	0.3828	0.2616	0.1673	0.0996	0.0547
3	0.9990	0.9872	0.9500	0.8791	0.7759	0.6496	0.5138	0.3823	0.2660	0.1719
4	0.9999	0.9984	0.9901	0.9672	0.9219	0.8497	0.7515	0.6331	0.5044	0.3770
5	1.0000	0.9999	0.9986	0.9936	0.9803	0.9527	0.9051	0.8338	0.7384	0.6230
6	1.0000	1.0000	0.9999	0.9991	0.9965	0.9894	0.9740	0.9452	0.8980	0.8281
7	1.0000	1.0000	1.0000	0.9999	0.9996	0.9984	0.9952	0.9877	0.9726	0.9453
8	1.0000	1.0000	1.0000	1.0000	1.0000	0.9999	0.9995	0.9983	0.9955	0.9893
9	1.0000	1.0000	1.0000	1.0000	1.0000	1.0000	1.0000	0.9999	0.9997	0.9990

S2

BINOMIAL CUMULATIVE DISTRIBUTION FUNCTION (continued)

$p =$	0.05	0.10	0.15	0.20	0.25	0.30	0.35	0.40	0.45	0.50
$n = 12, x = 0$	0.5404	0.2824	0.1422	0.0687	0.0317	0.0318	0.0057	0.0022	0.0008	0.0002
1	0.8816	0.6590	0.4435	0.2749	0.1584	0.0850	0.0424	0.0196	0.0083	0.0032
2	0.9804	0.8891	0.7358	0.5583	0.3907	0.2528	0.1513	0.0834	0.0421	0.0193
3	0.9978	0.9744	0.9078	0.7946	0.6488	0.4925	0.3467	0.2253	0.1345	0.0730
4	0.9998	0.9957	0.9761	0.9274	0.8424	0.7237	0.5833	0.4382	0.3044	0.1938
5	1.0000	0.9995	0.9954	0.9806	0.9456	0.8822	0.7873	0.6652	0.5269	0.3872
6	1.0000	0.9999	0.9993	0.9961	0.9857	0.9614	0.9154	0.8418	0.7393	0.6128
7	1.0000	1.0000	0.9999	0.9994	0.9972	0.9905	0.9745	0.9427	0.8883	0.8062
8	1.0000	1.0000	1.0000	0.9999	0.9996	0.9983	0.9944	0.9847	0.9644	0.9270
9	1.0000	1.0000	1.0000	1.0000	1.0000	0.9998	0.9992	0.9972	0.9921	0.9807
10	1.0000	1.0000	1.0000	1.0000	1.0000	1.0000	0.9999	0.9997	0.9989	0.9968
11	1.0000	1.0000	1.0000	1.0000	1.0000	1.0000	1.0000	1.0000	0.9999	0.9998
$n = 15, x = 0$	0.4633	0.2059	0.0874	0.0352	0.0134	0.0047	0.0016	0.0005	0.0001	0.0000
1	0.8290	0.5490	0.3186	0.1671	0.0802	0.0353	0.0142	0.0052	0.0017	0.0005
2	0.9638	0.8159	0.6042	0.3980	0.2361	0.1268	0.0617	0.0271	0.0107	0.0037
3	0.9945	0.9444	0.8227	0.6482	0.4613	0.2969	0.1727	0.0905	0.0424	0.0176
4	0.9994	0.9873	0.9383	0.8358	0.6865	0.5155	0.3519	0.2173	0.1204	0.0592
5	0.9999	0.9978	0.9832	0.9389	0.8516	0.7216	0.5643	0.4032	0.2608	0.1509
6	1.0000	0.9997	0.9964	0.9819	0.9434	0.8689	0.7548	0.6098	0.4522	0.3036
7	1.0000	1.0000	0.9994	0.9958	0.9827	0.9500	0.8868	0.7869	0.6535	0.5000
8	1.0000	1.0000	0.9999	0.9992	0.9958	0.9848	0.9578	0.9050	0.8182	0.6964
9	1.0000	1.0000	1.0000	0.9999	0.9992	0.9963	0.9876	0.9662	0.9231	0.8491
10	1.0000	1.0000	1.0000	1.0000	0.9999	0.9993	0.9972	0.9907	0.9745	0.9408
11	1.0000	1.0000	1.0000	1.0000	1.0000	0.9999	0.9995	0.9981	0.9937	0.9824
12	1.0000	1.0000	1.0000	1.0000	1.0000	1.0000	0.9999	0.9997	0.9989	0.9963
13	1.0000	1.0000	1.0000	1.0000	1.0000	1.0000	1.0000	1.0000	0.9999	0.9995
14	1.0000	1.0000	1.0000	1.0000	1.0000	1.0000	1.0000	1.0000	1.0000	1.0000
$n = 20, x = 0$	0.3585	0.1216	0.0388	0.0115	0.0032	0.0008	0.0002	0.0000	0.0000	0.0000
1	0.7358	0.3917	0.1756	0.0692	0.0243	0.0076	0.0021	0.0005	0.0001	0.0000
2	0.9245	0.6769	0.4049	0.2061	0.0913	0.0355	0.0121	0.0036	0.0009	0.0002
3	0.9841	0.8670	0.6477	0.4114	0.2252	0.1071	0.0444	0.0160	0.0049	0.0013
4	0.9974	0.9568	0.8298	0.6296	0.4148	0.2375	0.1182	0.0510	0.0189	0.0059
5	0.9997	0.9887	0.9327	0.8042	0.6172	0.4164	0.2454	0.1256	0.0553	0.0207
6	1.0000	0.9976	0.9781	0.9133	0.7858	0.6080	0.4166	0.2500	0.1299	0.0577
7	1.0000	0.9996	0.9941	0.9679	0.8982	0.7723	0.6010	0.4159	0.2520	0.1316
8	1.0000	0.9999	0.9987	0.9900	0.9591	0.8867	0.7624	0.5956	0.4143	0.2517
9	1.0000	1.0000	0.9998	0.9974	0.9861	0.9520	0.8782	0.7553	0.5914	0.4119
10	1.0000	1.0000	1.0000	0.9994	0.9961	0.9829	0.9468	0.8725	0.7507	0.5881
11	1.0000	1.0000	1.0000	0.9999	0.9991	0.9949	0.9804	0.9435	0.8692	0.7483
12	1.0000	1.0000	1.0000	1.0000	0.9998	0.9987	0.9940	0.9790	0.9420	0.8684
13	1.0000	1.0000	1.0000	1.0000	1.0000	0.9997	0.9985	0.9935	0.9786	0.9423
14	1.0000	1.0000	1.0000	1.0000	1.0000	1.0000	0.9997	0.9984	0.9936	0.9793
15	1.0000	1.0000	1.0000	1.0000	1.0000	1.0000	1.0000	0.9997	0.9985	0.9941
16	1.0000	1.0000	1.0000	1.0000	1.0000	1.0000	1.0000	1.0000	0.9997	0.9987
17	1.0000	1.0000	1.0000	1.0000	1.0000	1.0000	1.0000	1.0000	1.0000	0.9998
18	1.0000	1.0000	1.0000	1.0000	1.0000	1.0000	1.0000	1.0000	1.0000	1.0000

S2

BINOMIAL CUMULATIVE DISTRIBUTION FUNCTION (continued)

p =	0.05	0.10	0.15	0.20	0.25	0.30	0.35	0.40	0.45	0.50
n = 25, x = 0	0.2774	0.0718	0.0172	0.0038	0.0008	0.0001	0.0000	0.0000	0.0000	0.0000
1	0.6424	0.2712	0.0931	0.0274	0.0070	0.0016	0.0003	0.0001	0.0000	0.0000
2	0.8729	0.5371	0.2537	0.0982	0.0321	0.0090	0.0021	0.0004	0.0001	0.0000
3	0.9659	0.7636	0.4711	0.2340	0.0962	0.0332	0.0097	0.0024	0.0005	0.0001
4	0.9928	0.9020	0.6821	0.4207	0.2137	0.0905	0.0320	0.0095	0.0023	0.0005
5	0.9988	0.9666	0.8385	0.6167	0.3783	0.1935	0.0826	0.0294	0.0086	0.0020
6	0.9998	0.9905	0.9305	0.7800	0.5611	0.3407	0.1734	0.0736	0.0258	0.0073
7	1.0000	0.9977	0.9745	0.8909	0.7265	0.5118	0.3061	0.1536	0.0639	0.0216
8	1.0000	0.9995	0.9920	0.9532	0.8506	0.6769	0.4668	0.2735	0.1340	0.0539
9	1.0000	0.9999	0.9979	0.9827	0.9287	0.8106	0.6303	0.4246	0.2424	0.1148
10	1.0000	1.0000	0.9995	0.9944	0.9703	0.9022	0.7712	0.5858	0.3843	0.2122
11	1.0000	1.0000	0.9999	0.9985	0.9893	0.9558	0.8746	0.7323	0.5426	0.3450
12	1.0000	1.0000	1.0000	0.9996	0.9966	0.9825	0.9396	0.8462	0.6937	0.5000
13	1.0000	1.0000	1.0000	0.9999	0.9991	0.9940	0.9745	0.9222	0.8173	0.6550
14	1.0000	1.0000	1.0000	1.0000	0.9998	0.9982	0.9907	0.9656	0.9040	0.7878
15	1.0000	1.0000	1.0000	1.0000	1.0000	0.9995	0.9971	0.9868	0.9560	0.8852
16	1.0000	1.0000	1.0000	1.0000	1.0000	0.9999	0.9992	0.9957	0.9826	0.9461
17	1.0000	1.0000	1.0000	1.0000	1.0000	1.0000	0.9998	0.9988	0.9942	0.9784
18	1.0000	1.0000	1.0000	1.0000	1.0000	1.0000	1.0000	0.9997	0.9984	0.9927
19	1.0000	1.0000	1.0000	1.0000	1.0000	1.0000	1.0000	0.9999	0.9996	0.9980
20	1.0000	1.0000	1.0000	1.0000	1.0000	1.0000	1.0000	1.0000	0.9999	0.9995
21	1.0000	1.0000	1.0000	1.0000	1.0000	1.0000	1.0000	1.0000	1.0000	0.9999
22	1.0000	1.0000	1.0000	1.0000	1.0000	1.0000	1.0000	1.0000	1.0000	1.0000
n = 30, x = 0	0.2146	0.0424	0.0076	0.0012	0.0002	0.0000	0.0000	0.0000	0.0000	0.0000
1	0.5535	0.1837	0.0480	0.0105	0.0020	0.0003	0.0000	0.0000	0.0000	0.0000
2	0.8122	0.4114	0.1514	0.0442	0.0106	0.0021	0.0003	0.0000	0.0000	0.0000
3	0.9392	0.6474	0.3217	0.1227	0.0374	0.0093	0.0019	0.0003	0.0000	0.0000
4	0.9844	0.8245	0.5245	0.2552	0.0979	0.0302	0.0075	0.0015	0.0002	0.0000
5	0.9967	0.9268	0.7106	0.4275	0.2026	0.0766	0.0233	0.0057	0.0011	0.0002
6	0.9994	0.9742	0.8474	0.6070	0.3481	0.1595	0.0586	0.0172	0.0040	0.0007
7	0.9999	0.9922	0.9302	0.7608	0.5143	0.2814	0.1238	0.0435	0.0121	0.0026
8	1.0000	0.9980	0.9722	0.8713	0.6736	0.4315	0.2247	0.0940	0.0312	0.0081
9	1.0000	0.9995	0.9903	0.9389	0.8034	0.5888	0.3575	0.1763	0.0694	0.0214
10	1.0000	0.9999	0.9971	0.9744	0.8943	0.7304	0.5078	0.2915	0.1350	0.0494
11	1.0000	1.0000	0.9992	0.9905	0.9493	0.8407	0.6548	0.4311	0.2327	0.1002
12	1.0000	1.0000	0.9998	0.9969	0.9784	0.9155	0.7802	0.5785	0.3592	0.1808
13	1.0000	1.0000	1.0000	0.9991	0.9918	0.9599	0.8737	0.7145	0.5025	0.2923
14	1.0000	1.0000	1.0000	0.9998	0.9973	0.9831	0.9348	0.8246	0.6448	0.4278
15	1.0000	1.0000	1.0000	0.9999	0.9992	0.9936	0.9699	0.9029	0.7691	0.5722
16	1.0000	1.0000	1.0000	1.0000	0.9998	0.9979	0.9876	0.9519	0.8644	0.7077
17	1.0000	1.0000	1.0000	1.0000	0.9999	0.9994	0.9955	0.9788	0.9286	0.8192
18	1.0000	1.0000	1.0000	1.0000	1.0000	0.9998	0.9986	0.9917	0.9666	0.8998
19	1.0000	1.0000	1.0000	1.0000	1.0000	1.0000	0.9996	0.9971	0.9862	0.9506
20	1.0000	1.0000	1.0000	1.0000	1.0000	1.0000	0.9999	0.9991	0.9950	0.9786
21	1.0000	1.0000	1.0000	1.0000	1.0000	1.0000	1.0000	0.9998	0.9984	0.9919
22	1.0000	1.0000	1.0000	1.0000	1.0000	1.0000	1.0000	1.0000	0.9996	0.9974
23	1.0000	1.0000	1.0000	1.0000	1.0000	1.0000	1.0000	1.0000	0.9999	0.9993
24	1.0000	1.0000	1.0000	1.0000	1.0000	1.0000	1.0000	1.0000	1.0000	0.9998
25	1.0000	1.0000	1.0000	1.0000	1.0000	1.0000	1.0000	1.0000	1.0000	1.0000

S2

BINOMIAL CUMULATIVE DISTRIBUTION FUNCTION (continued)

p =	0.05	0.10	0.15	0.20	0.25	0.30	0.35	0.40	0.45	0.50
n = 40, x = 0	0.1285	0.0148	0.0015	0.0001	0.0000	0.0000	0.0000	0.0000	0.0000	0.0000
1	0.3991	0.0805	0.0121	0.0015	0.0001	0.0000	0.0000	0.0000	0.0000	0.0000
2	0.6767	0.2228	0.0486	0.0079	0.0010	0.0001	0.0000	0.0000	0.0000	0.0000
3	0.8619	0.4231	0.1302	0.0285	0.0047	0.0006	0.0001	0.0000	0.0000	0.0000
4	0.9520	0.6290	0.2633	0.0759	0.0160	0.0026	0.0003	0.0000	0.0000	0.0000
5	0.9861	0.7937	0.4325	0.1613	0.0433	0.0086	0.0013	0.0001	0.0000	0.0000
6	0.9966	0.9005	0.6067	0.2859	0.0962	0.0238	0.0044	0.0006	0.0001	0.0000
7	0.9993	0.9581	0.7559	0.4371	0.1820	0.0553	0.0124	0.0021	0.0002	0.0000
8	0.9999	0.9845	0.8646	0.5931	0.2998	0.1110	0.0303	0.0061	0.0009	0.0001
9	1.0000	0.9949	0.9328	0.7318	0.4395	0.1959	0.0644	0.0156	0.0027	0.0003
10	1.0000	0.9985	0.9701	0.8392	0.5839	0.3087	0.1215	0.0352	0.0074	0.0011
11	1.0000	0.9996	0.9880	0.9125	0.7151	0.4406	0.2053	0.0709	0.0179	0.0032
12	1.0000	0.9999	0.9957	0.9568	0.8209	0.5772	0.3143	0.1285	0.0386	0.0083
13	1.0000	1.0000	0.9986	0.9806	0.8968	0.7032	0.4408	0.2112	0.0751	0.0192
14	1.0000	1.0000	0.9996	0.9921	0.9456	0.8074	0.5721	0.3174	0.1326	0.0403
15	1.0000	1.0000	0.9999	0.9971	0.9738	0.8849	0.6946	0.4402	0.2142	0.0769
16	1.0000	1.0000	1.0000	0.9990	0.9884	0.9367	0.7978	0.5681	0.3185	0.1341
17	1.0000	1.0000	1.0000	0.9997	0.9953	0.9680	0.8761	0.6885	0.4391	0.2148
18	1.0000	1.0000	1.0000	0.9999	0.9983	0.9852	0.9301	0.7911	0.5651	0.3179
19	1.0000	1.0000	1.0000	1.0000	0.9994	0.9937	0.9637	0.8702	0.6844	0.4373
20	1.0000	1.0000	1.0000	1.0000	0.9998	0.9976	0.9827	0.9256	0.7870	0.5627
21	1.0000	1.0000	1.0000	1.0000	1.0000	0.9991	0.9925	0.9608	0.8669	0.6821
22	1.0000	1.0000	1.0000	1.0000	1.0000	0.9997	0.9970	0.9811	0.9233	0.7852
23	1.0000	1.0000	1.0000	1.0000	1.0000	0.9999	0.9989	0.9917	0.9595	0.8659
24	1.0000	1.0000	1.0000	1.0000	1.0000	1.0000	0.9996	0.9966	0.9804	0.9231
25	1.0000	1.0000	1.0000	1.0000	1.0000	1.0000	0.9999	0.9988	0.9914	0.9597
26	1.0000	1.0000	1.0000	1.0000	1.0000	1.0000	1.0000	0.9996	0.9966	0.9808
27	1.0000	1.0000	1.0000	1.0000	1.0000	1.0000	1.0000	0.9999	0.9988	0.9917
28	1.0000	1.0000	1.0000	1.0000	1.0000	1.0000	1.0000	1.0000	0.9996	0.9968
29	1.0000	1.0000	1.0000	1.0000	1.0000	1.0000	1.0000	1.0000	0.9999	0.9989
30	1.0000	1.0000	1.0000	1.0000	1.0000	1.0000	1.0000	1.0000	1.0000	0.9997
31	1.0000	1.0000	1.0000	1.0000	1.0000	1.0000	1.0000	1.0000	1.0000	0.9999
32	1.0000	1.0000	1.0000	1.0000	1.0000	1.0000	1.0000	1.0000	1.0000	1.0000
p =	0.05	0.10	0.15	0.20	0.25	0.30	0.35	0.40	0.45	0.50
n = 50, x = 0	0.0769	0.0052	0.0003	0.0000	0.0000	0.0000	0.0000	0.0000	0.0000	0.0000
1	0.2794	0.0338	0.0029	0.0002	0.0000	0.0000	0.0000	0.0000	0.0000	0.0000
2	0.5405	0.1117	0.0142	0.0013	0.0001	0.0000	0.0000	0.0000	0.0000	0.0000
3	0.7604	0.2503	0.0460	0.0057	0.0005	0.0000	0.0000	0.0000	0.0000	0.0000
4	0.8964	0.4312	0.1121	0.0185	0.0021	0.0002	0.0000	0.0000	0.0000	0.0000
5	0.9622	0.6161	0.2194	0.0480	0.0070	0.0007	0.0001	0.0000	0.0000	0.0000

S2

BINOMIAL CUMULATIVE DISTRIBUTION FUNCTION (continued)

6	0.9882	0.7702	0.3613	0.1034	0.0194	0.0025	0.0002	0.0000	0.0000	0.0000
7	0.9968	0.8779	0.5188	0.1904	0.0453	0.0073	0.0008	0.0001	0.0000	0.0000
8	0.9992	0.9421	0.6681	0.3073	0.0916	0.0183	0.0025	0.0002	0.0000	0.0000
9	0.9998	0.9755	0.7911	0.4437	0.1637	0.0402	0.0067	0.0008	0.0001	0.0000
10	1.0000	0.9906	0.8801	0.5836	0.2622	0.0789	0.0160	0.0022	0.0002	0.0000
11	1.0000	0.9968	0.9372	0.7107	0.3816	0.1390	0.0342	0.0057	0.0006	0.0000
12	1.0000	0.9990	0.9699	0.8139	0.5110	0.2229	0.0661	0.0133	0.0018	0.0002
13	1.0000	0.9997	0.9868	0.8894	0.6370	0.3279	0.1163	0.0280	0.0045	0.0005
14	1.0000	0.9999	0.9947	0.9393	0.7481	0.4468	0.1878	0.0540	0.0104	0.0013
15	1.0000	1.0000	0.9981	0.9692	0.8369	0.5692	0.2801	0.0955	0.0220	0.0033
16	1.0000	1.0000	0.9993	0.9856	0.9017	0.6839	0.3889	0.1561	0.0427	0.0077
17	1.0000	1.0000	0.9998	0.9937	0.9449	0.7822	0.5060	0.2369	0.0765	0.0164
18	1.0000	1.0000	0.9999	0.9975	0.9713	0.8594	0.6216	0.3356	0.1273	0.0325
19	1.0000	1.0000	1.0000	0.9991	0.9861	0.9152	0.7264	0.4465	0.1974	0.0595
20	1.0000	1.0000	1.0000	0.9997	0.9937	0.9522	0.8139	0.5610	0.2862	0.1013
21	1.0000	1.0000	1.0000	0.9999	0.9974	0.9749	0.8813	0.6701	0.3900	0.1611
22	1.0000	1.0000	1.0000	1.0000	0.9990	0.9877	0.9290	0.7660	0.5019	0.2399
23	1.0000	1.0000	1.0000	1.0000	0.9996	0.9944	0.9604	0.8438	0.6134	0.3359
24	1.0000	1.0000	1.0000	1.0000	0.9999	0.9976	0.9793	0.9022	0.7160	0.4439
25	1.0000	1.0000	1.0000	1.0000	1.0000	0.9991	0.9900	0.9427	0.8034	0.5561
26	1.0000	1.0000	1.0000	1.0000	1.0000	0.9997	0.9955	0.9686	0.8721	0.6641
27	1.0000	1.0000	1.0000	1.0000	1.0000	0.9999	0.9981	0.9840	0.9220	0.7601
28	1.0000	1.0000	1.0000	1.0000	1.0000	1.0000	0.9993	0.9924	0.9556	0.8389
29	1.0000	1.0000	1.0000	1.0000	1.0000	1.0000	0.9997	0.9966	0.9765	0.8987
30	1.0000	1.0000	1.0000	1.0000	1.0000	1.0000	0.9999	0.9986	0.9884	0.9405
31	1.0000	1.0000	1.0000	1.0000	1.0000	1.0000	1.0000	0.9995	0.9947	0.9675
32	1.0000	1.0000	1.0000	1.0000	1.0000	1.0000	1.0000	0.9998	0.9978	0.9836
33	1.0000	1.0000	1.0000	1.0000	1.0000	1.0000	1.0000	0.9999	0.9991	0.9923
34	1.0000	1.0000	1.0000	1.0000	1.0000	1.0000	1.0000	1.0000	0.9997	0.9967
35	1.0000	1.0000	1.0000	1.0000	1.0000	1.0000	1.0000	1.0000	0.9999	0.9987
36	1.0000	1.0000	1.0000	1.0000	1.0000	1.0000	1.0000	1.0000	1.0000	0.9995
37	1.0000	1.0000	1.0000	1.0000	1.0000	1.0000	1.0000	1.0000	1.0000	0.9998
38	1.0000	1.0000	1.0000	1.0000	1.0000	1.0000	1.0000	1.0000	1.0000	1.0000

S2

POISSON CUMULATIVE DISTRIBUTION FUNCTION

The tabulated value is $P(X \leqslant x)$, where X has a Poisson distribution with parameter λ.

$\lambda =$	0.5	1.0	1.5	2.0	2.5	3.0	3.5	4.0	4.5	5.0
$x = 0$	0.6065	0.3679	0.2231	0.1353	0.0821	0.0498	0.0302	0.0183	0.0111	0.0067
1	0.9098	0.7358	0.5578	0.4060	0.2873	0.1991	0.1359	0.0916	0.0611	0.0404
2	0.9856	0.9197	0.8088	0.6767	0.5438	0.4232	0.3208	0.2381	0.1736	0.1247
3	0.9982	0.9810	0.9344	0.8571	0.7576	0.6472	0.5366	0.4335	0.3423	0.2650
4	0.9998	0.9963	0.9814	0.9473	0.8912	0.8153	0.7254	0.6288	0.5321	0.4405
5	1.0000	0.9994	0.9955	0.9834	0.9580	0.9161	0.8576	0.7851	0.7029	0.6160
6	1.0000	0.9999	0.9991	0.9955	0.9858	0.9665	0.9347	0.8893	0.8311	0.7622
7	1.0000	1.0000	0.9998	0.9989	0.9958	0.9881	0.9733	0.9489	0.9134	0.8666
8	1.0000	1.0000	1.0000	0.9998	0.9989	0.9962	0.9901	0.9786	0.9597	0.9319
9	1.0000	1.0000	1.0000	1.0000	0.9997	0.9989	0.9967	0.9919	0.9829	0.9682
10	1.0000	1.0000	1.0000	1.0000	0.9999	0.9997	0.9990	0.9972	0.9933	0.9863
11	1.0000	1.0000	1.0000	1.0000	1.0000	0.9999	0.9997	0.9991	0.9976	0.9945
12	1.0000	1.0000	1.0000	1.0000	1.0000	1.0000	0.9999	0.9997	0.9992	0.9980
13	1.0000	1.0000	1.0000	1.0000	1.0000	1.0000	1.0000	0.9999	0.9997	0.9993
14	1.0000	1.0000	1.0000	1.0000	1.0000	1.0000	1.0000	1.0000	0.9999	0.9998
15	1.0000	1.0000	1.0000	1.0000	1.0000	1.0000	1.0000	1.0000	1.0000	0.9999
16	1.0000	1.0000	1.0000	1.0000	1.0000	1.0000	1.0000	1.0000	1.0000	1.0000
17	1.0000	1.0000	1.0000	1.0000	1.0000	1.0000	1.0000	1.0000	1.0000	1.0000
18	1.0000	1.0000	1.0000	1.0000	1.0000	1.0000	1.0000	1.0000	1.0000	1.0000
19	1.0000	1.0000	1.0000	1.0000	1.0000	1.0000	1.0000	1.0000	1.0000	1.0000

$\lambda =$	5.5	6.0	6.5	7.0	7.5	8.0	8.5	9.0	9.5	10.0
$x = 0$	0.0041	0.0025	0.0015	0.0009	0.0006	0.0003	0.0002	0.0001	0.0001	0.0000
1	0.0266	0.0174	0.0113	0.0073	0.0047	0.0030	0.0019	0.0012	0.0008	0.0005
2	0.0884	0.0620	0.0430	0.0296	0.0203	0.0138	0.0093	0.0062	0.0042	0.0028
3	0.2017	0.1512	0.1118	0.0818	0.0591	0.0424	0.0301	0.0212	0.0149	0.0103
4	0.3575	0.2851	0.2237	0.1730	0.1321	0.0996	0.0744	0.0550	0.0403	0.0293
5	0.5289	0.4457	0.3690	0.3007	0.2414	0.1912	0.1496	0.1157	0.0885	0.0671
6	0.6860	0.6063	0.5265	0.4497	0.3782	0.3134	0.2562	0.2068	0.1649	0.1301
7	0.8095	0.7440	0.6728	0.5987	0.5246	0.4530	0.3856	0.3239	0.2687	0.2202
8	0.8944	0.8472	0.7916	0.7291	0.6620	0.5925	0.5231	0.4557	0.3918	0.3328
9	0.9462	0.9161	0.8774	0.8305	0.7764	0.7166	0.6530	0.5874	0.5218	0.4579
10	0.9747	0.9574	0.9332	0.9015	0.8622	0.8159	0.7634	0.7060	0.6453	0.5830
11	0.9890	0.9799	0.9661	0.9467	0.9208	0.8881	0.8487	0.8030	0.7520	0.6968
12	0.9955	0.9912	0.9840	0.9730	0.9573	0.9362	0.9091	0.8758	0.8364	0.7916
13	0.9983	0.9964	0.9929	0.9872	0.9784	0.9658	0.9486	0.9261	0.8981	0.8645
14	0.9994	0.9986	0.9970	0.9943	0.9897	0.9827	0.9726	0.9585	0.9400	0.9165
15	0.9998	0.9995	0.9988	0.9976	0.9954	0.9918	0.9862	0.9780	0.9665	0.9513
16	0.9999	0.9998	0.9996	0.9990	0.9980	0.9963	0.9934	0.9889	0.9823	0.9730
17	1.0000	0.9999	0.9998	0.9996	0.9992	0.9984	0.9970	0.9947	0.9911	0.9857
18	1.0000	1.0000	0.9999	0.9999	0.9997	0.9993	0.9987	0.9976	0.9957	0.9928
19	1.0000	1.0000	1.0000	1.0000	0.9999	0.9997	0.9995	0.9989	0.9980	0.9965
20	1.0000	1.0000	1.0000	1.0000	1.0000	0.9999	0.9998	0.9996	0.9991	0.9984
21	1.0000	1.0000	1.0000	1.0000	1.0000	1.0000	0.9999	0.9998	0.9996	0.9993
22	1.0000	1.0000	1.0000	1.0000	1.0000	1.0000	1.0000	0.9999	0.9999	0.9997

Index

S2

WHICHURCH